The
Source

The Source

Eternal Design or Infinite Accident?

John N. Clayton

This book is dedicated to

Cynthia Ann Clayton.

– She was brought to me by God at a time when death had
taken my first wife Phyllis from me and when my pain
at that point was so great that I felt only my own death
would bring me happiness again.
– She has not only loved me out of my pain but has been
a fountain of enthusiasm and encouragement that has
changed me in a good way.
– She has stepped into a complex situation involving a con-
suming ministry and the shadow of my first wife. She
has done so with courage, a positive, dedicated, God-
centered spirit, and has brought joy and peace to me
and all who have been around her.
– She has renewed my enthusiasm and my desire to help
all who will listen and think to avoid the destructive
nature of atheism and doubt.
– Thank you Cynthia, for allowing God to use you to
renew this feeble man in a way that has made me far
more useful in my older years than I would have ever
dreamed possible.

John N. Clayton

CONTENTS

Illustrations		ix
Preface		xi
Introduction	The Need For Answers	1
Chapter 1	The Cosmos And the Creation	3
Chapter 2	The Design of Planet Earth	17
Chapter 3	Design in the Chemistry of Matter	29
Chapter 4	Design as Evidenced in Life	39
Chapter 5	The Nature of God	53
Chapter 6	Why Choose the Bible as the Word of God?	65
Chapter 7	Why —Is There Evil?	
	—Do We Exist?	
	—Do We Suffer?	85
Chapter 8	What about All Those Mistakes in the Bible?	95
Chapter 9	Evolution	103
Chapter 10	The Age of the Earth	113
Chapter 11	What Is Man?	137
Chapter 12	Conclusion	157
Appendix A		
	Checkable Biblical Accuracy	161
	The Scientific Accuracy of the Book of Mormon	164
	The Scientific Accuracy of the Koran	167

Appendix B

         Difficult Passages in the Koran   171

         Hindu Beliefs   178

         Basic Buddhism by Dalai Llama (6/01)   179

         Islam and Christianity Compared   180

Appendix 1   Calculated Odds for Being Suitably Located
         in Our Galaxy   183

Appendix 2   More on Universal Constants   185

Appendix 3   String Theory   189

Appendix 4   How Many Stars Are There?   191

Appendix 5   The Variable Nature of Time   193

Appendix 6   Evidence For Design in the Universe   195

Appendix 7   Hebrew Words And Definitions in Genesis
         1:1–31; 2:1–3   201

         Words and Definitions   207

Appendix 8   Animals of Genesis   211

         Sequence of Genesis   212

Appendix 9   Bibliography (as of March 2010)   213

References   223

Index   229

ILLUSTRATIONS

Figure 1.1: A spiral galaxy similar to the Milky Way, from the top, showing our solar system's approximate location   4

Figure 1.2: A spiral galaxy similar to the Milky Way, from the side, showing our solar system's approximate location   4

Figure 1.3: The speeds of the galaxies and their positions in space   7

Figure 1.4: Three galaxies over a period of time showing their relative positions   8

Figure 1.5: The fusion process on the sun   10

Figure 1.6: The sun in cross section   11

Figure 1.7: The logic flow of a cosmological argument   14

Figure 2.1: Four types of galaxies   20

Figure 2.2: The Milky Way galaxy, from the side, showing our solar system's location   20

Figure 2.3: The earth's orbit around the sun with the Northern Hemisphere tilted toward the sun in A and the Southern Hemisphere tilted toward the sun in B (exaggerated scale)   23

Figure 2.4: Estimated odds of selected variables vital to an earth-like planet occurring by chance   25

Figure 3.1: Big bang time line   33

Figure 3.2:   Water molecule if electrons were shared equally   34
Figure 3.3:   Actual water molecule displays design
              characteristics   34
Figure 3.4:   A graphic representation of the process of salt
              dissolving in water   35
Figure 3.5:   A possible arrangement of nonpolar water
              molecules in ice   36
Figure 3.6:   The actual structure of water molecules as ice
              forms   36
Figure 4.1:   The apparatus used by Stanley Miller to
              generate amino acids   42
Figure 5.1:   A sphere tangent to a plane produces a dot on
              the plane. The man in Flatland sees only the dot. 54
Figure 5.2:   A plane truncates a sphere. The man in
              Flatland sees a straight line.   55
Figure 5.3:   As the sphere moves through the plane, the
              apparent line gets smaller and smaller, until the
              man in Flatland once again sees only a dot.   55
Figure 9.1:   Lisa the geep … a cross between a goat and a
              sheep (a sheep-goat hybrid)   104
Figure 9:2:   Assumed biblical taxonomy of life   106
Figure 10.1: The tree of evolution from Chicago's Field
              Museum of Natural History   133
Figure 11.1: A baboon skeleton   139
Figure 11.2: An artist's concept of pliopithecus.   139
Figure 11.3: Proboscis monkey   140
Figure 11.4: How stone tools have changed over time   147
Figure 11.5: Physical attributes said to be unique to humans 149
Figure 11.6: Tim's Drawing   152
Figure 11.7: An artist's rendition of a chimpanzee drawing   153
Figure A1.1: Approximate doughnut-shaped area in a spiral
              galaxy where a solar system could exist   184
Figure A2.1: Example equations involving constants   186
Figure A2.2: Necessary universal constants   187
Figure A2.3: Example of polar bonds   187
Figure A4.1: The "Big Bang" view of the cosmos   192

PREFACE

It is not the intent of the author that this book be another effort at Christian Evidences. It is intended that this book be a functional part of an overall effort by the author and a team of other individuals to meet the doubts and problems of belief that many people have in today's world. It is the author's contention that a person does not need to leave his or her brains at home to be a Christian. We can intelligently and academically believe in God, and science can support such belief.

Our program is called **DOES GOD EXIST?** We offer audio and video materials, correspondence courses, booklets, and books to anyone searching for a basis of belief .This book is a part of this program. These materials are offered on a loan basis or at our cost. Because of the economy of production, this book is in a state of constant change—in fact, this is the sixth edition. We have aimed it at the average high school student, and some may find it too basic or too advanced for that reason. We ask for your input to this effort and your patience in some rough spots in the copy. As new discoveries and arguments come about, we will amend this effort. We also continually update documentation. If the reader finds documentation inadequate or dated, we encourage you to write us for the latest and most complete information.

We hope you find some stimulating ideas in this work, and that you will consider fairly the ideas presented. Some are a "thus saith the Lord" and others are "thus guesseth the author," but all are carefully thought out and tested through lectureships and discussions with others. We welcome your questions and encourage you to write us about them.

John N. Clayton

ACKNOWLEDGEMENTS

Grateful appreciation is sincerely felt by the author to Linda Glover, Julie Marcussen, and Karl Marcussen for their proofreading and contributions to this manuscript. My sincere thanks are also expressed to the many people who have provided encouragement, ideas, sources, and useful information which has been incorporated into this effort.

THE NEED FOR ANSWERS

"What intelligent person could possibly believe in an old man floating around up in the sky, blasting things into existence here on earth?" That was just one question I remember my mother asking me when I was a child.

My parents, Elizabeth and Stafford Clayton, were marvelous people. There was no divorce, no unfaithfulness, and no neglect in my family. As we did things together, my mother and father would ask me questions like the one above because both of them rejected the existence of a personal God, and they raised me to do the same.

From the beginning, I believed there was no God because of my parents' teaching. As I matured and observed the hypocritical lifestyle of many so-called Christians, I became more convinced than ever that only superstitious, ignorant, or self-serving people professed a belief in God. In retrospect, those who said they believed in God and the Bible and then lived a life in total defiance of or indifference to what God teaches did more to uphold the cause of atheism than the atheists themselves. Conversely, I knew that my life was consistent with what I believed, and what I believed was reasonable, logical, and certainly defendable.

What I hope to do in this book is to present to you the evidence and thinking that led me to change from an atheist with an inherited faith to not only become a believer in God, but a believer in Jesus Christ as God and in the Christian system and in the Bible as a guide to how we should live. However, in this discussion we will not start out with the Bible. When I tried to carry on a discussion with believers back in my atheist days, one of the things that used to frustrate me was the fact that they would begin the discussion by quoting scripture and somehow feel that the quoting of the Bible was going to impress me and change my mind! If God does not exist, then what is the Bible? Obviously it is the work of ancient ignorant people, and anything it says is either a reflection of that time or has been altered to keep up with new discoveries in science.

The first and most basic question is whether there is a God—any God out there. We will start with evidence from science and common sense to prove that there is a God, what the nature of the God is and has to be, and later which God it is that we are talking about. This discussion is about evidence and what a logical response to evidence has to be. It is not a Bible-thumping theological argument!

It is not just the religious fundamentalist that wants to bring out the Bible and hit people over the head with it. Atheists do the same thing but in a negative way. Atheists want to discuss social issues, mistakes in the Bible, or illogical actions of God as they see it all based on their reading and understanding of a particular translation of the Bible. The view seems to be that if a person can find something in the Bible that is wrong or impossible to accept, that somehow this has disproved the existence of God! That is a foolish approach. The Bible may offer some evidence as to which God we should be serving, how we should interpret the Bible, or a theological approach to a particular social issue, but it has nothing to do with the existence of God!

We want to start at the beginning or to be more exact, raise the question of whether there was a beginning.

Chapter 1

THE COSMOS AND THE CREATION

Those who like to indulge in philosophical debate might wish to contest the idea that any kind of existence is real. I have had skeptics ask me, "How do you know you exist?" This question reminds me of the story I heard about a father who called his son to ask how his college classes were going.

"Pretty well," said the son, "except philosophy."

"What's the problem there?" asked the father.

The son responded, "Well, every time the professor tries to call roll, we get into a debate about whether we really exist!"

"Absolute proof," in fact, does not exist for anything we do or even for our own existence itself. We are assuming that most people reading this material believe that they exist. We do not wish to quibble in our discussion about "absolute proof." With that as a starting assumption, all of us have a very limited choice about the origin of our existence. Either the matter from which the universe and we are made had a beginning or it did not have a beginning. There is no other reasonable choice possible (see figure 1.7, page 14).

COSMOLOGICAL FACTS

Any discussion about the origin of matter involves the very stuff of which the universe is made. As a result, we first need to review some basic cosmological facts before we can appreciate the arguments for whether or not matter had a beginning.

The following facts can be found in any basic astronomy book.

- The size of our galaxy and the tremendous size of the cosmos in general is essential to the survival of all we see. Without great distances between them, the stars, galaxies, planets, and the vast galactic clouds of matter that are all around us in space would be drawn together by gravitational attraction. Ultimately all matter would be reduced to one enormous blob of virtually infinite mass. So we need lots of space.

- The earth is part of a rotating system of planets that orbits a star we call the sun. The sun is but one of an estimated 100

Figure 1.1: A spiral galaxy similar to the Milky Way, from the top, showing our solar system's approximate location

© Anglo-Australian Observatory

Figure 1.2: A spiral galaxy similar to the Milky Way, from the side, showing our solar system's approximate location

© IAC/RGO/Main

billion stars all revolving in a spiral-shaped disk we refer to as the Milky Way galaxy (see figures 1.1 and 1.2).

The Xs in figures 1.1 and 1.2 show the approximate location of our solar system with its sun and all eight planets rotating around it. To get an idea of how big this system is, you could take the smallest pin you can find and poke a hole in the center of the X in figure 1.1. However, the tiny hole would be many times larger than *our entire solar system*. This experiment helps us to get a feel for the relative size of our earth when compared to our galaxy.

• Because the distances in space are so vast, scientists use a unit called the light-year to measure them. A light-year is the distance that light travels in one year. For example, our galaxy shown in figures 1.1 and 1.2 is approximately 100 thousand light-years in diameter. If we were to convert this number into miles, we would find that our galaxy is 588,000,000,000,000,000 miles across. (See the shaded box titled "Calculating the Diameter of Our Galaxy" to learn how that number is figured.)

Calculating the Diameter of Our Galaxy

Multiply the speed of light in a vacuum (186,317.6 miles per second) by the number of seconds in an hour (3,600) to get the speed in miles per hour.

Then multiply your answer by the number of hours in a day (23 hours, 56 minutes, 47 seconds).

When you get that worked out, multiply again by the number of days in a year (roughly 365.25) and you will have the distance that light travels in one year.

This number is approximately 5,880,000,000,000 miles, and it must be multiplied again by 100,000 (the diameter of the Milky Way) to get the diameter of our galaxy.

Thus we determine that the diameter of the galaxy is something on the order of 588,000,000,000,000,000 miles.

- Even this unfathomable number is microscopic when compared to the dimensions of the universe. If you were to take a very powerful telescope and look out into the constellation Hercules, you would see hundreds of hazy splotches of light.

  In 1997, the Hubble telescope looked into a region of space that was thought to be completely empty. Astronomers were astounded to see more splotches of light similar to the Hercules cluster. Each of those splotches of light is believed to be a galaxy up to 100,000 light-years in diameter and composed of 100 billion stars. We now know that there are millions of galaxies like these scattered across the seemingly endless space of the universe.

- Not surprisingly, our small segment of space contains two cloud-like galaxies called the large and small Magellanic Clouds, which are our closest neighbors. Another nearby galaxy, known as Andromeda, is about 2.2 million light-years from earth. It is very interesting to us because it is almost a twin to our own Milky Way galaxy except that it has a diameter twice as large ("Andromeda" 1998).

The following comparison will illustrate the magnitude of 2.2 million light-years. If you were to send a radio signal to a friend of yours living in Andromeda and your friend were to send you an answer the instant he received your message, you would have to wait at least 4,400,000 years for the reply. Remember that this message was sent both ways by one of the fastest transport systems we know—a radio wave that could orbit the earth over seven times in one second.

As we continue to look at properties of the cosmos, we need to discuss one fundamental concept that is vital to understanding the questions of cosmology and creation. That concept is whether the creation has always existed or whether it had a beginning. Many atheists have suggested that the universe did not have a beginning, that it is self-existing (the Humanist Manifesto—see References for the URL) and eternal in nature. This is a logical question for the atheist to raise because it simplifies their view of cosmology. If you admit to the fact that there was a beginning, then you are forced to deal in some way with the cause of that beginning. It is much simpler to just maintain that in some form or other the creation has always existed and there was no beginning to time, space, energy, or reality. Once you get into a discussion of cause, then the question of what did the causing has to be answered which again complicates the discussion.

Expanding Universe

The most incredible thing about the size of the universe discussed earlier is that it is getting larger with every passing second. If the universe is getting larger by expanding like a giant balloon, then the space between all the galaxies is also expanding. Look at figure 1.3 showing our galaxy and four others in relation to us. All of them are moving in the same general direction, but not at the same speed.

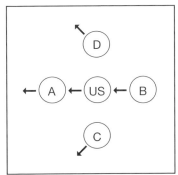

Figure 1.3: The speeds of the galaxies and their positions in space

If we are in the center (US) and moving to the left (←), galaxy A is moving faster than we are, since it is in front of us and also moving to the left. It is pulling away from us because it got a bigger push at the start.

Similarly, because galaxy B is behind us, it is moving in the same direction as we are, but at a slower speed. So we are likewise pulling away from it. Galaxies C and D are likely to be moving at the same speed along with us. However, since their trajectory relative to the center of the universe is different from ours, they would also appear to be pulling away from us. It is when we analyze all these different movement rates and directions that we conclude that the universe, in general, is expanding like a giant balloon.

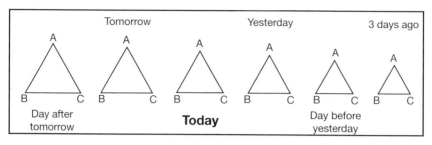

Figure 1.4: Three galaxies over a period of time showing their relative positions

With this in mind, let us consider another situation. Suppose that we observed three galaxies located at positions A, B, and C as illustrated in figure 1.4. If they are positioned in such a way that they form a triangle today, then they will form a bigger triangle tomorrow and a still bigger triangle the day after tomorrow, because the universe is becoming larger with every passing second.

In recent years astronomers have discovered something about the movement we are talking about that is absolutely incredible. Not only is the universe expanding, but it is accelerating in this expansion. Every galaxy in the cosmos is not only moving outward, but it is moving faster today than it was yesterday. Some mysterious force is accelerating the motion or at least accelerating the fabric of space in such a way that the cosmos is expanding faster and faster and faster. The energy that is doing this has been called "dark energy," mostly because we have no idea what it is. Whatever it is, the effect is the opposite of what we would expect. When you throw a ball up in the air it slows as it rises, eventually coming to a stop. What we are observing about the cosmos is that it would be like throwing a ball up in the air and having it go faster and faster as it moves away from us, never to be seen again.

Conversely, if we could run time backward, then yesterday the three galaxies would have been closer together than they are today, and even closer still the day before yesterday. As we keep going backward in time, obviously we will eventually end up at a point—a beginning—at what a physicist would call a singularity.

A good definition of a singularity is that it is a condition where the normal laws of Newtonian mechanics in physics do not apply. This is the world of quantum mechanics, a situation where the laws are different and where we are dealing with infinitely small quantities—the quantities that make up electrons, protons, and neutrons. We will talk more about this world and its laws shortly.

Big Bang

What logical interpretation can be made of this data? Even a casual look at figure 1.3 tells us that the pattern we observe is what some type of explosion would produce. That is why in 1929, the famous astronomer Edwin Hubble arrived at the same conclusion. His analysis led to the proposal of a "big bang" event as the origin of the cosmos. The actual term big bang was coined by Fred Hoyle in a 1950 BBC radio series entitled *The Nature of the Universe*. Since Hoyle believed the universe had always existed, he used the expression "big bang" to mock the theory that the universe had suddenly emerged. Ironically, the name caught on and subsequently became respectable (Barrow 1994, 34).

Today the big bang theory says that between 14 and 22 billion years ago, a singularity, suddenly and without any known explanation, became visible and produced something like a gigantic, seemingly controlled explosion. The content of this singularity, though being much smaller than a period on this page, contained the entire universe in energy form, including space itself. This pure energy rapidly expanded and was transformed, in accord with Einstein's theory, into all the galaxies, stars, and planets that we see about us.

In the 1990s, a number of supporting evidences for the big bang were discovered. The Cosmic Background Explorer project (COBE) found that temperature measurements of free space were exactly what a big bang event would produce (Dooling 1998). The distribution of galaxies and patterns of movement all agree with the big bang theory, leaving it as the best explanation we have for the distribution of the stars and galaxies we see in space.

If the big bang theory is accurate, does it support or deny God's existence as Creator? No matter how sophisticated this theory becomes, there are two fundamental questions that remain unanswered—What apparently exploded? and where did it come from? It should be evident, then, that the big bang theory does not explain creation.

Additionally, in the early 1990s, physical models of the big bang were developed that would not work until 10^{-43} seconds after it began (see figure 3.1, page 33). This is called Planck Time after the German theoretical physicist Max Karl Ernst Ludwig Planck. It marks the transition between the unknown and reality. There is currently no mathematical way to define matter before Planck Time. This has led Stephen Hawking, a world renowned theoretical physicist, to say that this period marked the beginning of both space and time. Before this instant, there is no way to explain physical relationships or to predict time-related, cause-and-effect phenomena. So if the big bang theory is correct, it proves that there was a beginning. However, as Hawking has also said, it offers no explanation for what blew up (Hawking 1988, 9). It only shows that matter is not eternal.

Amount of Hydrogen

Along with the big bang, there is other evidence indicating that the universe had a beginning. One example is the energy system of the cosmos. The sun is an incredible furnace made of its own fuel. Every second that passes allows 661 million tons of the sun's hydrogen to fuse into 657 million tons of helium, as shown in figures 1.5 and 1.6. The remaining 4 million tons of matter are released as energy in the form of electromagnetic radiation, which includes visible light (Audouze and Israel 1988, 24). In spite of this huge release of energy, the sun is only about 50% into its relevant life cycle. We know this by comparing the sun's gravity/mass with its energy/mass conversion rate. Though the sun can still supply useful heat for another five billion years, it is most reliable during the

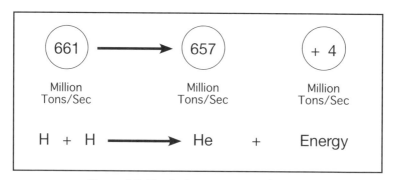

Figure 1.5: The fusion process on the sun

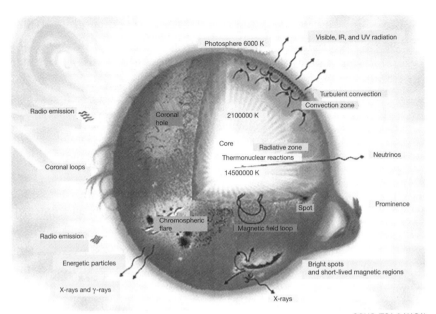

Figure 1.6: The sun in cross section

SOHO (ESA & NASA)

present mid life phase, which turns out to be absolutely essential for human life to survive.

Not only is the fusion of hydrogen the process that fires the sun, but it is also the starting process that drives all known energy reactions in space. Every star in every galaxy generates its energy by this same process. We know of no other energy production of any kind that can fire stars. If every star in the sky is using hydrogen as its basic fuel and if, as a result, multibillions of tons of hydrogen are being consumed per second all over the universe, what must be true of the total hydrogen supply in the cosmos? Hydrogen is a non-renewable resource. No process produces hydrogen from nothing, and it is the starting point for all elements in the periodic table.

What would happen if we were to fill up the gas tank in our car and drive and drive without putting in more gas? Obviously, we would soon come to an unavoidable stop. Likewise, if the universe has always been, we would long since have exhausted our hydrogen supply.

Nevertheless, hydrogen is still the most abundant material in the universe. We see it everywhere we look in space. In radio astronomy, the most common frequency received is 1,420 megacycles, which corresponds to the 21 centimeter wavelength of hydrogen as determined by a spectrometer. This is an express message from outer space indicating that enormous quantities of hydrogen are still out there.

Second Law of Thermodynamics

Another proof that the creation had a beginning is the second law of thermodynamics. It states that in a closed system, things tend to move toward a condition of disorder. For example, when you buy a new car, it is supposed to be in a perfect state. There are no loose nuts or bolts, no scratches or dents, no dirt, and no wear and tear on the engine or brakes.

What is the situation ten years later? The car has slowly become a disordered wreck. It has loose nuts and bolts, scratches, dents, wear and tear, and possibly will no longer run. When this happens, we say that the car has worn out or died. This process occurs in every aspect of our lives. Our bodies become disordered with age and ultimately death results. Chemists see this happening in atoms and molecules, and physicists and engineers can measure statistically the disorder of the systems with which they work.

However, these are not valid examples of a closed system. The car we described has had energy added to it with fuel, and a mechanic may have reversed some of the disorder by tightening loose bolts. Similarly, our bodies take in food and medicine and thus are not closed either. Even the earth is not a closed system, because it receives huge amounts of energy from the sun.

What about the universe? Is it a closed system? From an atheistic viewpoint, it would have to be, because there would be no outside source of energy available to renew it. In harmony with this viewpoint, Carl Sagan said, "The cosmos is everything that was, or is, or ever will be" (Sagan 1980, 257). This statement by the well-known atheist embodies a classic definition of a closed system. No organizing energy can be applied to a system that is defined as "everything that was, or is, or ever will be."

If that definition is accepted, what has to be true of the cosmos as far as the second law of thermodynamics is concerned? Clearly, since it is a closed system, it is obviously running down. As it ages, the available energy decreases and its disorder increases.

This means that the cosmos must have started sometime in the past because if the cosmos had always been here, it would now be totally disordered and freezing cold. Heat death would have set in, and we would not see any of the functional energy systems that make our existence possible. Therefore, thermodynamically, the universe had to have a beginning.

ATHEISTIC POSITION

Oscillating Universe

Over the centuries atheists have offered many objections to this discussion. One of those objections was to ask how we know we are not living in an eternally oscillating universe. Perhaps the universe expands outward until finally gravity slows down the expansion and everything comes to a stop. Gravity then begins a positive affect pulling everything back together to a singularity at which point the universe goes through another "big bang" and the process happens all over again.

There are so many problems with this proposal that it is not worthy of consideration. If all the mass of the cosmos was pulled back to a single point, you would have so much gravity that the cosmos would collapse into a massive black hole where gravity would simply overpower all other forces. The fact that the cosmos is accelerating in its expansion is a strong indication that gravitational collapse is not an option for the cosmos. As the cosmos accelerates and the distances become greater it becomes increasingly less likely that gravitation will have any significant effect on the eventual fate of the cosmos.

Another question that becomes an issue is whether quantum mechanics is disproving classical physics so that all of the discussions about cosmology and the conservation laws are null and void. We hear discussions about vacuum fluctuations and simultaneity presented as if they apply to modern cosmology. Quantum mechanics deals with the very small. When science talks about things like quarks, neutrinos, electrons, photons, mesons, and similar materials they are talking about quantum mechanics. The laws that govern these very small objects are different than the laws that govern things like galaxies. Sometimes mathematical predictions suggest things that are very strange to us, and many times suggestions are made that imply there are more dimensions than the X, Y, Z coordinates that we are familiar with. We will see shortly that the concept of dimensions is very useful to answering questions about God and the reality of God, but understand that the question of whether the creation of time, space, and energy had a beginning in our physical universe is not addressed by quantum mechanics. Later work may show some connections between these quantities, but the lesson of history is that when the information gets better understood it supports the concept of the existence of God.

Another point that needs to be made in discussions about quantum mechanics and things like vacuum fluctuations, parallel universes, and virtual universes is that many of these areas of discussion are not science. For something to be science it must be falsifiable—meaning it must be able to be tested. A person can propose anything, but if it cannot be tested in some way it is just a fantasy proposal and not a scientific proposal. When suggestions are made about parallel universes and eleven spacial dimensions the person making the proposal is advancing an interesting idea, but not something that is scientific and of value in understanding

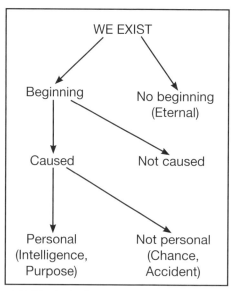

Figure 1.7: The logic flow of a cosmological argument

the world in which we live and how we are related to whatever is a challenge in our lives.

Certainly the discoveries of the future will improve our understanding of the details involved in these processes, but the fact that the universe will never collapse upon itself remains a solid proof that we had a beginning. With that in mind, we can use the chart in figure 1.7 as a guide in answering the next series of questions.

If the universe had a beginning, and we have every reason to believe it did according to the evidence, was that beginning caused or not caused? If it were caused, was the cause personal or nonpersonal? If it were a personal cause, we would expect certain attributes to be present in the creation, such as intelligence, purpose, design, and planning. If it were a nonpersonal cause, then none of these attributes would be found. Instead, the creation would be totally a product of chance, with no apparent purpose or intelligent reasoning behind it. So the next question to answer is, Do we have evidence supporting a design or a non-design hypothesis? That is the subject of our next chapter.

Chapter 2

THE DESIGN OF
PLANET EARTH

If we conclude that the universe had a beginning, we must then ask whether that beginning was caused or not caused. Believers maintain that the cosmos was created by God, clearly recognize that there was a cause and identify what that cause was (see figure 1.7, page 14).

This assertion contrasts sharply with those who would maintain that, out of an absolute void (no force, mass, or energy) and by an unknown principle of science, matter just popped into existence. Which of these explanations sounds the most plausible? First, we should ask if it is even possible for matter to come from nothing. The answer is no, not if we are going to be able to rely on the universal laws governing matter. This fact is critical to the question at hand, because from an atheistic point of view, these are the only laws there are.

Of these laws, certain ones are recognized as being the foundations of all scientific disciplines. The law of conservation of matter/energy, for example, is the foundation of chemistry. If matter can spontaneously pop into existence out of nothing, then the foundation of chemistry is compromised and no longer reliable.

The law of conservation of angular momentum is the foundation of most of the physical sciences, particularly classical physics. If matter can naturally come into existence out of nothing, endowed with the property of angular momentum, then all of physics is likewise uncertain and therefore unreliable.

Electronics is based upon the law of conservation of electrical charge. If matter possessing charges can mysteriously come into existence out of nothing, then all of electronics would be equally mysterious. There are many other conservation laws. In all cases, to accept the idea that matter was not caused means to deny that we can consistently rely on any scientific observation. Such a conclusion is not worthy of serious consideration if we are to think pragmatically and base our conclusions on available evidence.

Therefore, we can rationally conclude that the creation had a beginning and that the beginning was caused. So the final question remains, Was that cause personal or was it nonpersonal? If it were a personal cause, we would expect attributes like the Bible describes to be present in the creation—intelligence, purpose, design, and planning. If it were a nonpersonal cause, none of these attributes would be seen. The creation would be completely the product of chance, with no purpose or intelligence or reasoning behind it. It would be as Julian Huxley has written:

> We are as much a product of blind forces as is the falling of a stone to earth or the ebb and flow of the tides. We have just happened, and man was made flesh by a long series of singularly beneficial accidents (Smith 1976).

Whenever we use phrases like "just happened" or "a series of accidents" as Mr. Huxley did, we are speaking about the odds of something happening by chance alone. Since the probability of such events taking place by chance can be measured or predicted mathematically, we can test the reliability of these assertions.

CONDITIONS NECESSARY FOR A LIFE-SUPPORTING PLANET

Let us examine, then, a few of the variables necessary for producing a life-supporting planet and then calculate the mathematical probabilities of such a functional planet developing by chance alone from the big bang. First we will calculate the probability for each variable individually. At the end of our discussion, we will calculate the odds for all of the variables occurring simultaneously.

Normally, the calculations for probability would be based on many factors with regard to the entire universe. However, these calculations result in extremely large numbers that are not necessary to make the point. To keep the following probabilities smaller and simpler, we will use only a few familiar examples that are based on conservative, common-sense values.

The Right Kind of Galaxy

In a discussion about life in space, we need to realize that not all galaxies are the same. Figure 2.1 (page 20) shows four different kinds of galaxies.

Our galaxy, the Milky Way, is a type b spiral galaxy. That means our galaxy looks like a pinwheel of medium tightness in the winding of its arms. Interestingly, spiral galaxies are relatively rare in space.

Some eighty out of every one hundred galaxies are classified as elliptical galaxies. Unlike spiral galaxies, elliptical galaxies are made up of older stars and contain very little dust and only limited amounts of other solid materials. There is nothing in an elliptical galaxy from which to produce a planet, let alone to make life to put on that planet.

Similar problems exist for the other types of galaxies listed, as well as some we have not listed. Seyfert galaxies, for example, explode every so often, shattering everything in and around them. There is good evidence available showing that well under 1% of all galaxies in space have the conditions necessary to sustain life. If we accept a figure of 1%, that means that the odds of having the big bang produce the right kind of galaxy by chance alone are 1 in 100.

The Right Position in the Galaxy

Figure 2.2 (page 20) demonstrates that the position of our earth in the galaxy is essential to our survival. The sketch is a side view of our galaxy as seen from a great distance in space. The X marks the position of our solar system within the Milky Way galaxy. Throughout most of our galaxy, the gravitational and magnetic

Spiral

Elliptical

Irregular

Barred spiral

Figure 2.1: Four types of galaxies

© Anglo-Australian Observatory

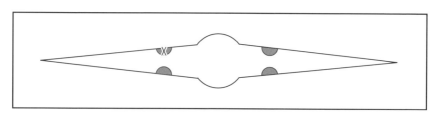

Figure 2.2: The Milky Way galaxy, from the side,
showing our solar system's location

forces are so intense that a solar system like ours could not remain intact.

Only in two doughnut-shaped areas called galactic habitable zones (GHZ) located outside the central bulge of the galaxy could a solar system like ours safely exist. In figure 2.2, these "doughnuts" are shaded in to emphasize their approximate location. Taking the calculated volume of our galaxy and dividing it by the volume of the shaded areas gives a value of approximately 150 (see appendix 1, page 183). Therefore, the odds of having a solar system located in one of those doughnuts are 1 in 150.

The Right Kind of Star

Another factor we must include in our calculations relates to the kind of star needed to serve as the sun of our solar system. Of the 100 billion stars in any given galaxy, only a very small percent would be identical or nearly identical to our sun with the proper size, radiation, and temperature needed to support the kinds of systems found on the earth. For instance, the Hubble telescope revealed in 1996 that 70% of all stars are red dwarfs, 10% are white dwarfs, and 15% are K dwarfs. That means that 95% of all stars are too small and cold to support a functional solar system.

Someone might respond that this should not be a factor because a planet could simply be closer to a colder star. However, there is a limit to how close a star can be to a planet without its gravitational force destroying the planet. This limit is called Roche's Limit. It is the closest distance in which a planet can be situated from its parent star (sun) and not be torn apart by tidal bulges developed within its crustal skin.

Dwarf stars would require a planet to be too close to survive, because the planet would have to be inside Roche's Limit to be warm enough to support life as we know it. With the elimination of all 95% of the suspected dwarf stars from our calculation, we are left with about 5 billion (5% of 100 billion) stars in our galaxy that may include a sun like ours.

A significant number of these remaining stars would also include binary or trinary stars, blue stars, and red giants like Betelgeuse in the Orion constellation. Binary or trinary groups are multiple stars orbiting one another. They, too, would destroy any planetary satellite like our earth. Because blue stars emit too much destructive heat and radiation and red giants are much too large, they would not qualify as eligible substitutes for our sun either.

The star we need would have to be just hot enough to allow for a suitable planet to orbit outside Roche's Limit and yet be at a distance that would sustain life-supporting temperatures. Therefore, if we generously assume that 100 million of the remaining 5 billion stars were possible replacements for our sun, we would have a galactic probability ratio of 1 to 1,000.

The Right Distance from the Sun

Studies of Venus have shown that our distance from the sun is critical to the existence of life. Venus is a near twin to the earth in many ways, but its closeness to the sun and its slow, backward rotation rate have left the planet with a dense cloud cover made out of sulfuric acid, causing ground temperatures to rise up to 900°F.

Earth's distance from the sun also becomes crucial when we consider how important water is for sustaining life. For water to exist in a liquid state, a very specific temperature range must be maintained. The freezing point of water is 32°F (0°C) and its boiling point is 212°F (100°C). This requires that our distance to the sun has to be a distance that will keep the average ground temperature well above 32° at night and significantly below 212° during the day. This distance is called the circumstellar habitable zone (CHZ) within a solar system.

If we were any closer to the sun than we are, all of our water would be in the vapor state. If we were any farther away from the sun than we are, our water would exist only as solid ice. Since there are ten planets in our solar system (counting the asteroid belt as a planet and still counting Pluto), only one of these ten is at the right distance for water to continuously exist as a liquid. Based upon this, we could conservatively say that the odds of having a planet the right distance from the sun are 1 in 10.

The Right Planetary Tilt

Another essential design feature is the tilt or inclination of the earth's axis. This tilt, along with the distribution of landmasses and the chemical properties of water, is also critical to maintaining a reliable range of temperatures on the earth's surface.

In figure 2.3, we see a sketch of the shape of the earth's orbit around the sun. Our summer in the Northern Hemisphere occurs when the earth is at point A. Notice that we are farther from the sun at this time.

At point B, we see the situation is quite different during summer in the Southern Hemisphere. The earth is closer to the sun than it was at point A. It would seem, then, that there would be a great deal more heat accumulated in the Southern Hemisphere during its summer than there would be in the Northern Hemisphere. This is, in fact, what would happen if there were not two significant design features incorporated within the earth's physical makeup to prevent

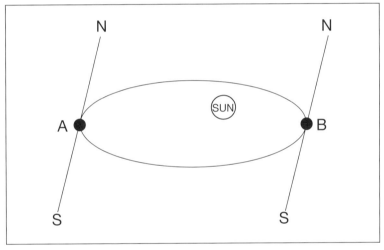

Figure 2.3: The earth's orbit around the sun with the Northern Hemisphere tilted toward the sun in A and the Southern Hemisphere tilted toward the sun in B (exaggerated scale)

it—the distribution of landmasses and the heat retention properties of land and water.

The Right Land-and-Water Distribution

A casual look at any world map shows that most of the landmass of planet earth is in the Northern Hemisphere. This naturally leaves most of the Southern Hemisphere covered by water. Water has a large heat capacity, whereas land does not. This means that water both absorbs and releases a lot of heat slowly. Landmasses, on the other hand, do just the opposite.

Therefore, when the Southern Hemisphere is close to the sun, most of the sun's intense heat is dissipated when it reflects off the water. Some of the heat that the water does absorb is circulated to the colder Northern Hemisphere by ocean currents. If water were not concentrated in the Southern Hemisphere, this heat dissipation and transfer system would not work.

These two properties, working in conjunction with the earth's tilted axis, help to moderate global temperatures. The northern landmass area absorbs maximum solar energy when the earth is farthest from the sun, while the southern waters both store and reflect heat when the earth is closest.

It is because of earth's tilt and the complementary heat retaining properties of land and water that we experience the four seasons and other climatic variations essential to life. Since these combined features are unique to planet earth, the odds of them occurring in our solar system are again 1 in 10.

More Right Conditions for the Earth

Mars has demonstrated for us what a thin atmosphere does to help shape a planet's surface. Neil Cummins of the astronomy department at the University of Maine has shown that, without a large solitary moon, a planet cannot maintain the tilt of its axis critical to the mixing of atmospheric gases—another factor that has apparently rendered Mars inhospitable for life. Our studies of the atmospheres of other planets have proven how carefully designed our earth is, with some twenty-six different atmospheric layers, each serving a separate function essential to preserving life.

In addition, charged particles raining down from space, from the sun, and from other stars are repelled by the earth's magnetic field. This may be our most important shielding device next to the atmosphere itself. Again, using our solar system as a basis, the odds of these three features happening by chance are 1 in 10, respectively.

We have also discovered that our supermassive planets of Jupiter, Saturn, Uranus, and Neptune passively serve a vital purpose as they use their huge gravitational fields to draw invading comets away from possible collisions with earth. We conservatively give this a probability factor of 1 in 40.

Finally, no life-bearing planet or system could exist anywhere near a black hole. As we have already discussed in chapter 1, because of a black hole's tremendous gravitational field, not even light can escape from it. Our only evidence of its existence is that we see matter being swallowed up by it. If a black hole came near a star like our sun, it would instantly destroy both the sun and our earth, along with all the other planets in our solar system. We estimate that the odds of a planet not being near a black hole are less than 1 in 250.

Thus far, we have discussed only a few of the necessary conditions needed for our planet to support life. While there are many more we could mention, the ones we have considered are sufficient to prove our point. For a listing of other variables see Appendix 6 (page 195). Figure 2.4 summarizes eleven of the more obvious essential characteristics, along with the odds of their occurring by chance alone.

Being in the right kind of galaxy .... 1 in 100
Being in the right place in the galaxy .... 1 in 150
Having the right kind of star .... 1 in 1,000
Being the right distance from the star .... 1 in 10
Having the proper planetary mass .... 1 in 10
Having the proper planetary spin .... 1 in 10
Having the proper planetary tilt .... 1 in 10
Having comet-sweeping planets .... 1 in 40
Not being near a black hole .... 1 in 250
Having a large solitary moon .... 1 in 10
Possessing a magnetic field
    capable of shielding .... 1 in 10

Total Odds .... 1 in 150,000,000,000,000,000

Figure 2.4: Estimated odds of selected variables vital to an earth-like planet occurring by chance

PROBABILITIES FOR CHANCE PRODUCING A LIFE-SUPPORTING PLANET

At this point, someone might say, "These odds are all well within the realm of possibility, so you are proving very little by listing them." This is certainly true. All of these events could possibly have happened individually. In the case of a life-supporting planet, however, they all must be happening at the same time and place, which changes things considerably.

How to Figure Probabilities

In order to appreciate how small the probabilities become when so many events must take place simultaneously, we need to review a few basic rules of probability. If I have a deck of cards that is thoroughly shuffled, and I ask you to draw the ace of spades blindly from the deck, what are the probabilities of your doing so? One out of fifty-two (1/52). Now suppose I ask you to draw the ace of spades twice in a row, shuffling the deck each time.

In other words, you draw the ace, I shuffle it back into the deck, and you draw it again — twice in a row. What are the odds now? The answer is 1/52 x 1/52 or 1/2,704. When two things have to occur in a row or simultaneously, you multiply the individual probabilities together. The odds of drawing the same ace four times in a row would be 1/52 x 1/52 x 1/52 x 1/52, which equals 1 in 7,311,616.

Let us consider the short list of probabilities for each variable in figure 2.4. We can now use it to calculate the odds of having all of the beneficial features occurring together to produce a life-supporting planet. Like the cards, all these conditions have to be satisfied simultaneously or in a row, so to speak. We have to multiply all the odds or probabilities together as we did with the cards. Even with these very conservative figures, the probabilities would be 1 in 150 thousand million million (1.5×10^{17}).

This figure includes only a few of the conditions necessary to support life on the earth. It does not include all the other precise chemical balances needed in the composition of the atom and the elements making up matter. And it does not include the factors needed for life itself, as demonstrated in its complex chemical codes for DNA and RNA.

Odds for Betting a Life

However, with just this small sample of eleven necessary characteristics we have used here, we find the odds for a chance occurrence are far greater than anything we humans would care to bet our lives on. For example, parachute clubs have often stated that the odds of surviving a fall without a parachute from 10,000 feet are 1 in 10 million.

If I offered you a billion dollars (tax free) to jump out of an airplane at 10,000 feet without a parachute, with the proviso that you had to live to collect it, would you accept the offer? Not if you were in your right mind, I am sure. Obviously, the odds of survival are much too small for any rational person to accept. Yet the odds of there being an "accidental" planet hospitable for life using only the few parameters we have considered are 15 *billion* times less likely than surviving a free-fall from an airplane.

One of the most famous atheists of the twentieth century was Antony Flew. Flew had debated apologists for Christianity many times, had written numerous books, and was considered the best atheist scholar in the world during the last half of the twentieth century. In May 2004, Flew told a symposium at New York State University that he had changed his mind and he now believed in God. His statement was:

> What I think the DNA material has done is that it has shown, by the almost unbelievable complexity of the arrangements which are needed to produce (life), that intelligence must have been involved in getting these extraordinary diverse elements to work together. It's the enormous complexity of the number of elements and the enormous subtlety of the ways they work together. The meeting of these two parts at the right time by chance is simply minute. It is all a matter of the enormous complexity by which the results were achieved, which looked to me like the work of intelligence (Flew 2007, 75).

Chapter 3

DESIGN IN THE CHEMISTRY OF MATTER

Before one of the billions of galaxies in the expanding universe could provide the perfect location for our planet earth to support life, matter had to come into existence. By "matter" we mean atoms and molecules, the forces binding them together, and the laws governing their interactions. A brief examination of what scientists believe took place regarding the creation of matter within the first few seconds and then minutes of the big bang will add even more convincing proof of intelligent design inherent in creation.

THE FOUR FUNDAMENTAL FORCES

All matter in our universe is composed of atoms. Each atom contains a certain number of neutrons, protons, and electrons, which are themselves made of even smaller units. These smaller units—quarks, neutrinos, etc.—are governed by the laws of quantum mechanics and make up charge. For the sake of simplicity, we will ignore these smaller units and just focus on the three classic components: the neutron, proton, and electron.

Everything that happens in the universe and in our world is based upon the interaction of atoms combining with other atoms to form molecules. The forces that bind together particles within the atom, that control all the possible combinations of atoms, and that determine their rates of decay are known as the four fundamental forces of physics.

These forces can be expressed mathematically in the basic equations of physics. There are a number of physical constants that show up in these equations which must be *very* precise for matter to exist in a way that can sustain life. This precision becomes obvious with a closer examination of the four forces.

The Strong Force

The strong force does not reach far—only the distance across a single atom—but it serves as the glue of the universe. It is the force that holds the protons and neutrons together in the nucleus of the atom.

The precise strength of this force is crucial for the existence of life. If it were any weaker, atoms would not form at all. If it were stronger, all matter could conceivably clump together into one giant nucleus.

The Weak Force

The weak force works interactively with the strong force and has to do with radioactive decay of elements. It is 100,000 times weaker than the strong force and works over very short distances. This confines its action to individual subatomic particles. Nevertheless, the delicate disturbances it makes cause a neutron to transmute into a proton, which results in the production of elements like nitrogen, oxygen, and carbon, all of which are vital for life.

The Electromagnetic Force

Each of the building blocks of the atom has a different electrical charge. The proton has a positive charge, the electron has a negative charge, and the neutron is neutral. Both electricity and magnetism demonstrate that like charges repel and opposite charges attract.

It is the electromagnetic force that keeps the negatively charged electrons orbiting the positively charged nucleus of the atom. If this electromagnetic force were any weaker, electrons would fly off into space and the atom would not exist. If it were any stronger, electrons would be bound so tightly to the nucleus they could not be shared with other atoms. As a result, no molecules would be able to form.

Not only are the strong force and the electromagnetic force precisely balanced individually, they have also been beautifully designed to work together as a team within the atom. The strong force on its own should draw multiple protons in the nucleus together into one lump. What keeps them distinct?

Since like charges repel and all protons are positively charged, the electromagnetic repulsion force keeps the protons separated from each other. The atom, all molecules, and life itself hang in this perfect balance of forces. (See appendix 2, page 185.) (Note: In the late 1960s and early 1970s, the electromagnetic and weak forces were mathematically merged into the single "electroweak force.")

Gravity

While everything in the universe is subject to the force of gravity, it is more relevant in this discussion to describe the effect of gravity on large objects, such as stars and planets in space (quantum mechanics and nuclear physics are striving to explain what gravity is). We could say that gravity is to the universe as the strong force is to the atom. Gravity is at least some of the glue that holds galaxies together.

The strength of the force of gravity depends upon the separation distance and the respective mass of objects (how many protons and neutrons they contain). The greater the mass, the more gravity it produces. That is why the sun, which is very massive, exerts such a strong attraction on the earth, as well as all the other planets revolving around it. (See appendix 2, page 185.)

We have said that the strong force in the atom is balanced by electromagnetism, which keeps the protons from clumping together. In the universe, however, the balancing factor preventing gravity from attracting all matter into one gigantic clump is the relative expanding motion caused by the big bang.

If the initial acceleration from the big bang had been any less, the force of gravity would have consolidated everything before any discrete galaxies could have formed. Conversely, if the explosive force of the big bang had been even slightly greater, the gravitational force would not have been strong enough to pull atoms together.

As it is, the delicate balance between gravity and the expansive motion is perfect—just right for matter and, finally, for galaxies to form.

THE BIG BANG TIME LINE

As scientists try to reconstruct a history that would fit all of these forces together they theorize that all the matter of the universe was compressed into an infinitesimally small point called a singularity. Time and space would have been created and immediately after the start of its explosive expansion, it is believed that all four of the fundamental forces were united in a single force referred to as the Unified Force. There were no atoms or particles, only energy that was *very, very* hot (10^{29} K [On the Kelvin (K) temperature scale, 0 K marks absolute zero, 273 K marks the freezing point of water, and 373 K marks the boiling point of water in metric degrees.]).

Figure 3.1 illustrates the order and approximate time periods in which the cataclysmic events took place.

Notice the period representing the *first second* after the big bang. Within that first second, through a highly complex process involving many transitional events, the Unified Force split into the four fundamental forces we discussed, and the *exact number* of discrete electrons, protons, and neutrons formed. In this arrangement, protons and electrons form first, with neutrons to follow. Neutrons are nothing more than a proton and an electron compressed together.

Scientists who study quantum mechanics presently believe that the basic properties necessary to unite these fundamental forces need at least seven other dimensions in order to produce matter as we know it. The necessity for these other dimensions has important implications for the existence and domain of God, as we will discuss in chapter 5. (See appendix 3 for additional information, page 189.)

Three minutes after the big bang, the universe had cooled enough for protons and neutrons to unite and form nuclei. By 300,000 years, the universal temperature had cooled to 3,000 K, allowing the first simple atoms like hydrogen and helium to form. Since then, for the past 10 to 20 billion years, the universe as we know it with stars, galaxies, and planets has been expanding into what we see today.

It is important to note here that some people mistakenly view this process as being godless evolution. This is certainly not the case, any more than it would be to explain the existence of the great pyramids in Egypt. Just because something takes a long time to build does not mean it was caused by evolution. There is nothing unpredictably random or unplanned about the building of either the great pyramids or the universe. The precision with which the various components of the universe are formed is truly amazing and clearly manifests the "finger of God" in all that has been accomplished (Psalm 8:3).

This is exemplified by the extremely delicate balancing of the four fundamental forces that came into existence within the *first second* of the big bang event. After that, at least twenty-eight other equally fine-tuned characteristics had to occur regarding matter in order to produce our present universe and life itself. If we attribute the big

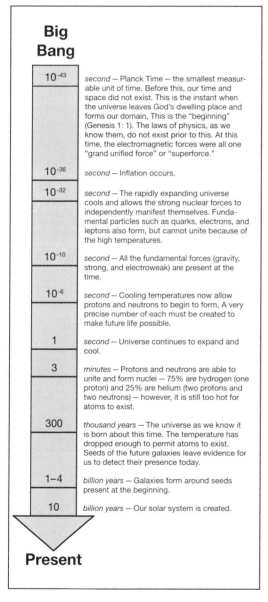

Big Bang

10^{-43} second — Planck Time — the smallest measurable unit of time. Before this, our time and space did not exist. This is the instant when the universe leaves God's dwelling place and forms our domain, This is the "beginning" (Genesis 1: 1). The laws of physics, as we know them, do not exist prior to this. At this time, the electromagnetic forces were all one "grand unified force" or "superforce."

10^{-36} second — Inflation occurs.

10^{-32} second — The rapidly expanding universe cools and allows the strong nuclear forces to independently manifest themselves. Fundamental particles such as quarks, electrons, and leptons also form, but cannot unite because of the high temperatures.

10^{-10} second — All the fundamental forces (gravity, strong, and electroweak) are present at the time.

10^{-6} second — Cooling temperatures now allow protons and neutrons to begin to form, A very precise number of each must be created to make future life possible.

1 second — Universe continues to expand and cool.

3 minutes — Protons and neutrons are able to unite and form nuclei — 75% are hydrogen (one proton) and 25% are helium (two protons and two neutrons) — however, it is still too hot for atoms to exist.

300 thousand years — The universe as we know it is born about this time. The temperature has dropped enough to permit atoms to exist. Seeds of the future galaxies leave evidence for us to detect their presence today.

1–4 billion years — Galaxies form around seeds present at the beginning.

10 billion years — Our solar system is created.

Present

Figure 3.1: Big bang time line

bang to blind, unintelligent chance, how could all of the various constants (fine-tuned numerical relationships) have arrived at such precise values on the very first try? For instance, the unusual structure of the water molecule well illustrates the effect of the perfect balance between forces, along with the obvious intervention of a designer/creator, God.

THE WATER MOLECULE

At first glance, the water molecule seems to be very simple. It is made up of only two elements, hydrogen and oxygen. In one water molecule, two atoms of hydrogen share electrons with one atom of oxygen (H_2O). Often molecules share electrons equally. If this were true for water, the arrangement of the atoms would look like the illustration in figure 3.2. The oxygen would be tightly bound by hydrogen.

However, because both the oxygen and hydrogen atoms have room for an extra electron within their inner orbital shells, they bind together differently. Since oxygen has a more massive nucleus, its attraction for electrons is greater than that of hydrogen. As a result, there is an angle of 105° between the hydrogen atoms, as pictured in figure 3.3.

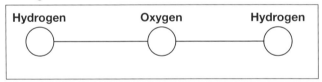

Figure 3.2: Water molecule if electrons were shared equally

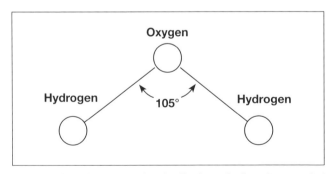

Figure 3.3: Actual water molecule displays design characteristics

Solvency Property

One immediate result of this arrangement (called a polar arrangement) is that it allows water to dissolve things. Salt, for example, has the chemical formula Na (sodium) Cl (chloride). When salt is placed in water, the sodium is pulled toward the oxygen end of the water molecule and the chloride toward the hydrogen end, as shown in figure 3.4.

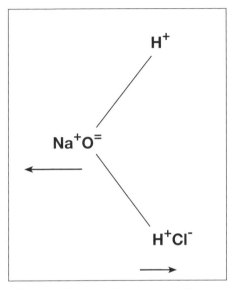

Figure 3.4: A graphic representation of the process of salt dissolving in water

This dissolving process causes the sodium chloride molecule to be torn apart by its attraction to both hydrogen and oxygen. If the water molecule were arranged as shown in figure 3.2, the oxygen atom would be too tightly bound to the hydrogen to attract the sodium, so the salt would not dissolve.

This solvency property of water is very important. Nutrients in the soil must be dissolved in water before they can be absorbed by plants. The blood in our bodies is 83% water, and it carries dissolved nutrients to all parts of our bodies. A drop of rainwater falling through the air dissolves atmospheric gases, affecting the quality of our land, lakes, and rivers. In other words, all life on earth depends upon this very unusual design feature of the water molecule.

Freezing Property

As if that were not enough, the way water freezes is another manifestation of its unusual atomic arrangement. Water is one of the few materials in nature that freezes from the top down. Most liquids become more dense as they cool, and they sink in the process. Water does, too, until it reaches 40°F (4°C). At this temperature, the water molecules begin to lock on to each other, forming ice crystals.

If water were nonpolar, its rearrangement into ice might look like that shown in figure 3.5. With the polar structure water actually possesses, the distribution of frozen water molecules looks like that shown in figure 3.6.

This latter arrangement takes up more space, which means that its density is less. For this reason, ice floats and forms on the surface of the water instead of at the bottom.

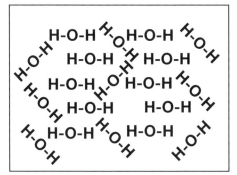

Figure 3.5: A possible arrangement of nonpolar water molecules in ice

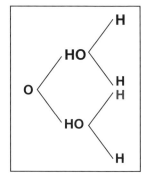

Figure 3.6: The actual structure of water molecules as ice forms

The importance of water freezing from the top down may not be obvious at first glance. Think of the consequences, though, if water froze from the bottom up. First of all, it would allow year-round evaporation, since water evaporates much more rapidly than ice. The climate changes caused by the extra moisture in the air would be severe in areas near large bodies of water.

Second, and even more important, many animals living in saltwater or freshwater environments would not be able to survive. Their food supply and much of their protection from predators would be eliminated. Third, icebergs would not float. Ice would sink to the bottom where colder water temperatures would allow it to accumulate over time, upsetting currents in the sea that depend upon uninhibited convection.

This brief review should make it obvious that life on earth is dependent upon the unusual design features of the atoms in the water molecule. Rather than believing that the cosmos began by pure chance, would it not be more reasonable to recognize that the powerful hand of an engineering God carefully crafted every design feature? If this is evident in the formation of the universe, it is even more evident in the creation of life, as we shall see in the next chapter.

Chapter 4

DESIGN AS EVIDENCED IN LIFE

A simple examination of the material making up the universe shows intelligent design in the perfect balance found to exist among all the natural forces. In like manner, the complexities inherent in life on this earth testify to the powerful, personal hand of an engineering God who has mathematically expressed his design features in every exquisite detail.

DESIGN WITHIN THE CELL

Definition of life

In order to appreciate the design in life, we first need to define exactly what we mean when we say "life." Do we mean an organism that can move, eat, breathe, reproduce, and respond to external stimuli? The problem with that definition is that some living bacteria do not breathe and some nonliving molecules reproduce. To resolve the problem, we will define life as consisting of three essential components. (1) A living organism must be enclosed by a membrane or skin that separates it from its environment. (2) The organism must contain information molecules, such as deoxyribonucleic acid (DNA) and ribonucleic acid (RNA). (3) The organism must possess the chemical tools with which it can replicate itself on the cellular level.

This definition shows that life is irreducibly complex. If anyone of the three components is missing, life does not exist. So if it can be proven that even one of the above essentials could not form by random occurrence, then life itself could not come into existence by chance. Since so much research has been done in recent years on DNA and RNA, we will focus on the second component for life listed above.

The Complexity of the Cell

Back in Darwin's time when it was believed that the cell was nothing more than a simple blob of protoplasm, it was much easier for biologists to assume that the first cells had evolved from basic chemicals rather quickly and easily. Scientists made a series of what they then considered relatively small leaps from primordial soup to simple molecules to more complex molecules to a cell membrane to a cell. From a cell, they figured that life would proliferate in earnest.

These simplistic assumptions can no longer be made. We now know that a single cell with a nucleus is the microscopic equivalent of an entire high-tech, industrialized city. It is surrounded by a wall armed with a tight security system, selectively allowing raw materials to enter and manufactured products to leave. The city contains a factory in production around the clock, tied to a trillion other similar factories by a mysterious communications network that dictates repair schedules and keeps track of all inventory.

A special library within each city is filled with detailed blueprints for every piece of machinery and maintenance equipment it uses. In living organisms, this information includes every minute characteristic of the organism, from the number of hairs on a human body to the shape, size, and function of every organ, including the unique pattern of each fingerprint.

Directions for all of this activity are encoded in DNA, the genetic material of each cell, that is wound into the shape of a double helix within the microscopically small nucleus. DNA also supplies detailed instructions on how to make and distribute all the necessary complex proteins that organisms need to use as building materials and as enzymes to carry out millions of functions that keep the host organism alive and healthy. This process is called protein synthesis, a highly sophisticated, intricately designed process that takes place trillions of times a day within the cells of a human body.

To make matters even more complicated, the "language" of DNA is expressed in chemicals that are called nucleotides, and the "language" of proteins is expressed in chemical complexes called amino acids. To manufacture proteins, a translation from one language to the other is necessary. This is where the RNA molecules come in. They translate the four nucleotides of DNA into the twenty amino acids used to build proteins. These twenty amino acids combine in unique configurations to produce thousands of proteins. (For more information, see the shaded box titled "Meters of DNA in the Human Cell.")

Stanley Miller's Experiment

With this newfound knowledge of the complexity of the cell, scientists have had a much more difficult problem in explaining how the cell could possibly have come into existence by chance. In an attempt to solve this problem, they thought about how to synthesize amino acids, because amino acids are the building blocks of proteins, and proteins are essential for life.

With this goal in mind, in 1953, a graduate student at the University of Chicago named Stanley Miller simulated in the laboratory the atmospheric gases he believed had existed soon after the earth's formation three or four billion years ago. (We should note here that those assumptions he made about the composition of

Meters of DNA in the Human Cell

A human cell contains about 2 meters of DNA. The human body is composed of approximately 10^{13} cells, and therefore contains about 2 times 10^{13} meters of DNA. Some idea of extreme length of this DNA can be understood by comparing it with the distance from the earth to the sun, which is 1.5 times 10^{11} meters. That means that the DNA in our bodies could stretch to the sun and back about 50 times.

How efficiently is this DNA packed into each cell? The 2 meters of DNA in a human is packed into 46 chromosomes, all in a nucleus 0.006 millimeters in diameter! (Griffiths et al. 1993, 468).

earth's atmosphere back in 1953 appear to be no longer valid, based on current evidence. The materials chosen were chosen because of their chemical properties, not from any evidence that they were present in the earth's history.)

To the gases contained in the apparatus shown in figure 4.1, Miller added a pool of water and an electric current to correspond to lightning, which could have acted as an energy source on the primitive earth. After boiling the water and sparking the gases for about a week, he found that the reddish water produced contained several kinds of amino acids. It appeared that the early earth could have had the potential for producing life-supporting proteins by natural means.

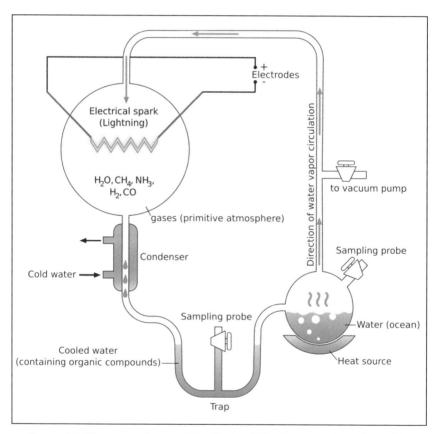

Figure 4.1: The apparatus used by Stanley Miller to generate amino acids

Probabilities for Protein

As a result of that experiment, over 50 years ago, we would expect that by now there would be a mountain of evidence showing the possible progression from amino acids to complex proteins, along with promising research relating to the emergence of RNA and DNA. Instead, researchers using the best equipment available to simulate conditions on the prebiotic (lifeless) earth have continually failed to naturally produce even one essential protein from random combinations of amino acids. Why?

Peter Radetsky comments on this question in *Earth* magazine.

Today his [Miller's] scenario is regarded with misgivings. One reason is that geologists now think that the primordial atmosphere consisted mainly of carbon dioxide and nitrogen gases that are less reactive than those used in the 1953 experiment. And even if Miller's atmosphere could have existed, how do you get simple molecules such as amino acids to go through the necessary chemical changes that will convert them into more complicated compounds, or polymers, such as proteins? Miller himself throws up his hands at that part of the puzzle. "It's a problem," he sighs with exasperation. "How do you make polymers? That's not so easy" (1998, 34).

We might ask, then, based upon probabilities, how easy would it be for a protein to randomly form in nature? Biologists tell us the odds are one chance in 10^{160} (1 with 160 zeros after it). Applying chemical kinetics, this would require something like 10^{243} years for one occurrence. (This number was originally in *Evolution: Possible or Impossible* [Coppedge, 1976]. In recent years similar calculations have been released by other authors. See our bibliography in appendix 9, page 213: Behe, Dembski, Lester and Bohlin, Ross and Rana, Collins, and Spetner.)

Yet the fossil record appears to give evidence of *completed cells* (not merely proteins) functioning within 100 to 500 million years after the primitive earth cooled enough to allow for stable chemical reactions to take place. Some are even saying now that chemical life must have evolved, not in millions of years, but in thousands.

However, according to the laws of probability, even 500 million years is not nearly enough time for the natural development of such a complicated structure as the cell. Mathematicians generally agree that anything with a probability of less than one in 10^{50} is

---

Linear Sequence of an E. coli Protein

								10										20

Met- Glu- Arg- Tyr- Glu- Ser- Leu- Phe- Ala- Gln- Leu- Lys- Glu- Arg- Lys- Glu- Gly- Ala- Phe- Val-

30   40

Pro- Phe- Val- Thr- Leu- Gly- Asp- Pro- Gly- Ile- Glu- Gln- Ser- Leu- Lys- Ile- Ile- Asp- Thr- Leu-

50   60

Ile- Glu- Ala- Gly- Ala- Asp- Ala- Leu- Glu- Leu- Gly- Ile- Pro- Phe- Ser- Asp- Pro- Leu- Ala- Asp-

70   80

Gly- Pro- Thr- Ile- Gln- Asn- Ala- Thr- Leu- Arg- Ala- Phe- Ala- Ala- Gly- Val- Thr- Pro- Ala- Gln-

90   100

Cys- Phe- Glu- Met- Leu- Ala- Leu- Ile- Arg- Gln- Lys- His- Pro- Thr- Ile- Pro- Ile- Gly- Leu- Leu-

110   120

Met- Tyr- Ala- Asn- Leu- Val- Phe- Asn- Lys- Gly- Ile- Asp- Glu- Phe- Tyr- Ala- Gln- Cys- Glu- Lys-

130   140

Val- Gly- Val- Asp- Ser- Val- Leu- Val- Ala- Asp- Val- Pro- Val- Gln- Glu- Ser- Ala- Pro- Phe- Arg-

150   160

Gln- Ala- Ala- Leu- Arg- His- Asn- Val- Ala- Pro- Ile- Phe- Ile- Cys- Pro- Pro- Asn- Ala- Asp- Asp-

170   180

Asp- Leu- Leu- Arg- Gln- Ile- Ala- Ser- Tyr- Gly- Arg- Gly- Tyr- Thr- Tyr- Leu- Leu- Ser- Arg- Ala-

190   200

Gly- Val- Thr- Gly- Ala- Glu- Asn- Arg- Ala- Ala- Leu- Pro- Leu- Asn- His- Leu- Val- Ala- Lys- Leu-

210   220

Lys- Glu- Tyr- Asn- Ala- Ala- Pro- Pro- Leu- Gln- Gly- Phe- Gly- Ile- Ser- Ala- Pro- Asp- Gln- Val-

230   240

Lys- Ala- Ala- Ile- Asp- Ala- Gly- Ala- Ala- Gly- Ala- Ile- Ser- Gly- Ser- Ala- Ile- Val- Lys- Ile-

250   260

Ile- Glu- Gln- His- Asn- Ile- Glu- Pro- Glu- Lys- Met- Leu- Ala- Ala- Leu- Lys- Val- Phe- Val- Gln-

268

Pro- Met- Lys- Ala- Ala- Thr- Arg- Ser-

Linear sequence of one protein called the E. coli tryptophan synthetase protein. It is made up of 268 amino acids that must bond to each other in the precise order listed above. Notice how similar the arrangement is to a computer program. If such an encoded message were received from outer space, there would be no doubt the intelligence of the sender. Yet some scientists want us to believe that the entire cell including this sophisticated message came about by random chance.

equivalent to total impossibility. The figure, then, of 1 in 10^{160} puts the odds of one protein occurring by chance far beyond what any rational person could accept. And one protein is a far cry from the complexities of life.

As scientists have recognized the need to borrow more time, they have proposed theories suggesting that life arrived on earth from outer space, either on a spaceship or in cometary dust. However, as Christian de Duve commented, "Even if life came from elsewhere, we would still have to account for its first development. Thus we might as well assume that life started on earth" (1995, 1). Needless to say, with that assumption, the problem of insufficient time still looms as large as ever.

For Christians, the idea that life came to earth from outer space makes perfect sense, if by "outer space" we mean from a source beyond our universe. The Bible is silent regarding the existence of any other life in the material universe, which means at present there is no information available to us one way or the other. But the Bible is far from silent regarding the source of all life in the person of God, whose dwelling is outside the bounds of the universe he created.

One rebuttal to the arguments we have been presenting is to say that, no matter what the odds are, in an infinite universe, it will happen. Yet as enormous as the cosmos is, it is neither infinitely large nor infinitely old. Calculations show that there are not enough stars in the cosmos to allow chance to be a working factor in explaining the design we see (see appendix 4, page 191).

DESIGN IN NATURE

So far our discussion of design has concentrated on statistics showing that chance alone cannot adequately explain the creation as we understand it. Another approach is to review the evidence for design found in nature. While we cannot readily put numbers on such evidence, we can appeal to the common sense and fairness of the observer.

For example, watching the birth of a baby can be an awe-inspiring experience that may speak powerfully to some observers about the Creator's plan and design. The skeptic will regard this awesome event as simply an example of conformity to the laws of nature. For many of us, that explanation does not go far enough. More is needed to explain the complexity often found in the natural world. The following examples will help us see the skillful hand of a master designer manifest within and among the various species found in the world around us.

Evolution

The ability of life as a whole to adapt to a changing earth shows features that strongly suggest a designer. The built-in number of available mutation points in life's genetic coding is critical for the continued survival of the species. These mutation points are just one of the ways an animal's DNA is able to change quickly to meet new environmental demands.

Fortunately, the genetic composition of life is designed so that when climate changes, oceans advance, vegetation is modified, or predators are introduced, life can adapt and go on. This ability to change is called evolution. Without it, life would have disappeared from the earth long ago.

A classic example of this kind of design is present in humans themselves. As far as we know, humans originated in tropical climate areas. We have every reason to believe that earth's original men and women possessed considerable amounts of an adaptive skin pigment called melanin. This genetically determined material is important to the survival of humans near the equator.

One advantage of differing skin color is the ability to release heat by radiation. A totally black can filled with boiling water will cool faster that an identical white can filled with the same water. At equatorial latitudes there is a need to release heat quickly, so having dark skin pigmentation in equatorial areas is a huge advantage. In a polar area on the other hand, you do not want to release heat by any method at all, and having white skin is a major advantage in a cold climate. There are other advantages to differences in skin pigmentation.

Dark pigmentation gives protection against solar radiation, ultraviolet light, skin cancer, and/or vitamin D poisoning. When the sun shines on a white person, all of the components of the sun's radiation are absorbed into the person's metabolism. In a black person, however, the sun's radiation products are absorbed into the melanin of his or her skin, thus avoiding sun poisoning.

For this reason, people living at the equator who have white skin need external protection, or they cannot survive. Black people, though, are ideally suited for that environment. Even a casual look reveals to us the "latitude effect" on skin color. With some exceptions, as one moves north from the Congo to Egypt, Palestine, Greece, Portugal, Germany, and Sweden, the skin color gets lighter, the eye color bluer, and the hair color blonder. Genetic evidence has added to the view that all humans descended from one female ancestor, whom even the scientists have called "Mother Eve." If all humans share a common female ancestor and yet there are multiple races on the earth, it is obvious that all humans have evolved and adapted to their various environments.

The point of all this, of course, is that if humans had not been created with the ability to adapt or, as many scientists would say, to evolve, they could never have left the environment of their origin. This evolutionary design feature is too wonderfully arranged to be attributed to chance and is, therefore, clear evidence of design.

Symbiosis

One area that strongly resists a totally natural explanation is the area of symbiotic relationships. A symbiotic relationship is one in which two organisms live in such a close relationship that one cannot live without the other and vice versa. Certain plants cannot live without certain insects that pollinate them or clean them or store up certain nutrients for them. At the same time, the plant provides nourishment and/or protection for the insect. Sometimes such relationships exist between two plants or two animals, like the Portuguese man o' war "jellyfish" and the tiny fish that live among its tentacles and yet never get stung. These types of two-way symbiotic relationships are difficult to explain by natural causes because the question automatically arises, which came first?

If you agree that there are problems answering this question with two codependent life forms, how much more difficult do you think it would be to explain the simultaneous evolution of three? Yet this is what we find with a leaf-cutting ant species in South America whose colonies may contain up to eight million ants, a number which surprisingly represents the collective biomass of an adult cow.

These particular ants cultivate mushrooms as a farmer cultivates crops, using leaf cuttings instead of soil. The ants are not able to eat the leaves because the leaves contain a natural insecticide. Neither can the mushrooms live on the leaves because the surface of the leaves is coated with a prohibitive wax.

To make the relationship work, the ants must carefully avoid the poison as they scrape the wax off the leaves. Without the wax, the leaves are able to decay into a mulch in which the mushrooms can grow. The mushrooms, in turn, harmlessly absorb the insecticide, converting it into an edible food for the ants called gongylidia. Neither creature could live without the other. Scientists have known about the dual nature of this symbiosis for a long time.

However, recent studies have revealed another partner necessary to sustain the ant/mushroom relationship (Schultz 1999, 747–748; Currie et al. 1999, 701–704). The mushrooms have a parasite enemy that would normally destroy them, but they can be protected with an antibiotic produced by a special bacterium that, coincidentally, lives on the ants' bodies. So the bacterium depends upon the host ant's body for life. The ant depends upon the food produced by the mushrooms for life. And the mushrooms depend upon the ants' farming practices and the ants' pet bacterium for life.

This three-way relationship is irreducibly complex. If anyone of the partners is missing, the entire group dies. The only way such a codependent society could be produced is by intelligent design. Any other attempted explanation quickly becomes a quest for the impossible dream.

Ecosystematic Design

In this day of ecological concern, nearly everyone is aware of the many delicate balances maintained in nature. Minor changes in one part of an ecological system can adversely affect the whole system. Therefore, it is very important that critical, life-supporting functions be reliable. Such reliability should be convincing evidence of design, as shown in the following examples.

Photosynthesis

Photosynthesis is the fundamental support for all life on earth. It is not only the starting point for all food chains through its amazing use of light and inorganic chemicals to generate organic food materials, but it also produces the oxygen needed for animal life to continue to exist.

Because we now understand the chemical instability of the whole photosynthetic process and its susceptibility to outside disturbances, we should be impressed with an intricacy of design that clearly could not have happened by accident. To hypothesize that by some strange series of natural processes a system such as this was created by chance is more unbelievable than expecting DNA to arise by chance in Stanley Miller's apparatus. Instead, it is far more probable that this universal supporter of all ecosystems is the product of the creator or designer of the cosmos.

Unique Animal Adaptations

Everyone is familiar with the ability of air conditioners to keep us cool on hot summer days. Air conditioners use a type of heat exchanger that allows warm air to flow through a cold radiator-like device and cool the air. Some animals are equipped with similar heat-exchanging systems that, instead of cooling them, help to conserve their body heat because they live in extremely cold environments.

For example, birds wading in cold water can lose a lot of heat through their legs. Arctic animals like seals, dolphins, and whales can lose life-supporting heat through their flippers. The tongues of gray whales also face a problem with heat loss when cold Arctic water rushes over them as the whales feed. Because there is very little insulating fat on their tongues, the potential for heat loss is critically high. How do the whales survive?

The actual heat exchanger in animals is called rete mirabile and is comprised of two layers of blood vessels (arteries and veins) that flow in opposite directions. As the cold blood leaves an exposed organ, such as the whale's flipper or tongue, it comes very close to a dense layer of blood vessels traveling in the opposite direction. This allows the warm blood leaving the animal's body and entering the flipper or tongue to transfer much of its heat to the returning cold blood.

How efficient is this heat transferring system? In regard to the whale's tongue, researchers have found that the tongue loses less heat than the rest of the whale's heavily insulated body. Without such a heat exchanger, the whale could not survive. Is this just a coincidence? Air-conditioning systems do not just happen by chance. Living heat exchangers are yet another example of intelligent design in nature (Heyning and Mead 1997, 1138–1139; see also Schmidt-Nielsen 1997).

Without a designer, it is difficult to explain how the angler fish got the wormlike appendage it suspends in front of itself to attract other fish within its "gobbling range." How did it survive before it got its built-in fishing tackle?

The same question arises about the archer fish that spits streams of water at insects, knocking them out of the trees above the water so it can catch and eat them. The amazing feature this fish possesses is its special set of bifocal eyes that allows it to see above and below the water at the same time. Without these special eyes, it could never hit its target. Which came first, the ability to spit or the ability to see in both media?

There have been evolutionary hypotheses advanced to explain some of these behaviors, but they require so many imaginary and conditional explanations that they become unbelievable. Skeptics like Richard Dawkins believe that if they can give an evolutionary chance explanation for design features such as these, no matter how imaginative or bizarre, they have destroyed the design argument (1986). However, just giving a possible explanation does not prove anything. It is only a vague faith-based conjecture or guess and not a convincing proof that evolutionary chance is the causal agent.

Instinct

Probably the most obvious examples of creative design are the instincts of animals and insects. Instinct may be defined as a behavioral characteristic inherent in a living organism that is neither learned nor accomplished by conscious thought. So ingenious and sophisticated are these instincts in animals that they clearly show they are the work of a designer. Intuitively, it should be apparent that such instincts could not have been developed by a step-by-step process based upon random chance.

For instance, marsupial mammals (animals with pouches) demonstrate a nearly miraculous instinct just by being born. Within a few weeks after conception, the fetus of a kangaroo comes into the world. Even though it is still only partially formed and well under an inch long, it crawls from the uterine environment to the belly pouch in which it will live until it is nearly an adult.

This long journey (many, many times the baby's body length) is accomplished totally without sight and without any learning or help from its mother. The only equipment the tiny creature possesses is its unusually developed, strong forelimbs and claws. During its incredible journey and while it is maturing in the pouch, its younger brothers and sisters, conceived at the same time, are put on hold in the mother's womb until the new baby either dies or leaves as an adult. At that time, one of the waiting siblings then resumes its development by making another long and arduous trip up the mother's belly.

Instinct is equally remarkable in the navigational systems of animals. Birds and turtles can travel thousands of miles in all kinds of weather and to places they have never been before. They are known to successfully return to their place of birth, even though they may have been removed from that location long before they were old enough to know where they were. How can such abilities be acquired? Not by random chance, but by built-in design features inherent in the animals.

Even more simple forms like bees and ants show truly remarkable evidence of design in their instincts. Of all the engineering shapes humans can use to build structures, there is only one recognized to be optimum in both cost and strength—the hexagon. Humans have come to this conclusion by a trial-and-error process. Various structural shapes have been subjected to stress analyses, using complex mathematical calculations, including calculus, to examine the results. The bee, however, has been constructing a hexagonal structure in the most economical way from the beginning. Trial-and-error learning for the bee would have been fatal.

Instincts, then, clearly show evidence of design. They are unlearned yet precise. They are specific features arranged for a particular ecosystem, and their design can be of tremendous sophistication. If we recognize these as design features, then we must concede the existence of an intelligent designer, a God who is solely responsible for creating all life and its remarkable complexities.

At this point, if we look back at figure 1.7 (page 14), we can continue our logical argument for the existence of God. So far in our discussion, we have shown that scientific evidence supports the Bible's position that there was a beginning to the creation. If there was a beginning, then logically there had to be a cause or a causer. Through our brief examination of nature, we have seen that the causer is a superior intellectual being who incorporated intelligence, reasoning, planning, design, and order into all that he created. We have not made this point by arguing religiously, but rather on the basis of scientific evidence. The next logical step, then, is to explore the nature of that intelligence, which we will do in the following chapter.

Chapter 5

THE NATURE OF GOD

If the arguments presented so far in this discussion have provided convincing evidence for the existence of a Creator, the question that naturally follows would be: If there is a God, who or what kind of being is he? Unfortunately, many people throughout history have anthropomorphized God by using features limited by our time and space environment to define and describe him.

They ask questions such as, What color of skin does God have? What sex is God? How can God hear my prayers and the prayers of a man in China at the same time? Where did God come from? Is God dead, as some have claimed? Or, as the Russian cosmonaut asked, "Why didn't I see God while I was in orbit?" Attributing these human characteristics to God has caused atheists to accuse believers of creating God in their image to fill their need for security and hope.

Not only has this misconception of God contributed to the apparent atheistic cause that abounds in the world, but it is also a major cause for religious division. God should not be described in this way. God should be understood as a being outside our universe in another dimension.

THE ANALOGY OF FLATLAND

In order to illustrate the problems associated with visualizing another dimension beyond our three-dimensional world of length, width, and height, Edwin Abbott wrote a book titled *Flatland* in which a two-dimensional man lives on a sheet of paper that comprises his two-dimensional world. On the surface of the paper, there is only length and width. There is no such thing as thickness or height. We see the man living there as a profile only. He cannot rotate his neck in any way to see above the front surface or below the back surface of the paper.

Application to Another Dimension

Setting the Scene

One day, the man in Flatland is visited by a sphere, which has a three-dimensional shape. It crosses Flatland at right angles in the man's living room, and he is incredulous. Just as a tennis ball dipped in paint and touched to a sheet of paper would produce a dot on that paper, so, too, the movement of the sphere touching the surface of Flatland would at first only produce a dot (see figure 5.1).

Figure 5.1: A sphere tangent to a plane produces a dot on the plane. The man in Flatland sees only the dot.

Drawing by Katherine Cody Kicklighter

The dot appears with no apparent cause from the man's viewpoint. A dot in Flatland is considered to be solid matter. The man himself is made up of a series of dots. That is what a line is. As far as he is concerned, matter has just appeared out of nothing, much like the concept of the singularity scientists use to explain the big bang.

From our perspective, the dot becomes a circle that keeps growing in size as the sphere passes through the plane (see figure 5.2).

Figure 5.2: A plane truncates a sphere. The man in Flatland sees a straight line. Drawing by Katherine Cody Kicklighter

After penetrating as far as its equator, the circle then becomes progressively smaller until it turns back into a dot once again, just before it disappears (see figure 5.3). However, because our man is only a two-dimensional character, he does not actually see a circle. He only sees a dot grow into a line and then contract back into a dot again before disappearing.

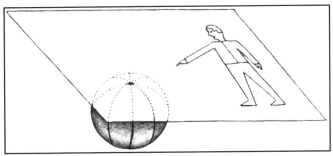

Figure 5.3: As the sphere moves through the plane, the apparent line gets smaller and smaller, until the man in Flatland once again sees only a dot. Drawing by Katherine Cody Kicklighter

The man is terrified because he does not understand what is happening. All of the laws of science that state that matter cannot be created or destroyed have been violated. What he sees is for him a true miracle.

Speaking to the Sphere

Suppose now that the man in Flatland decides to talk to the sphere before it completes its passage through the plane. Talking to a sphere is a unique experience in itself, because its voice comes from all around the man and even from inside him as the sound waves cross his plane. After recovering from this strange encounter, the man asks, "What are you?"

The sphere says, "I'll show you. Draw a circle on your floor."

This is not easy for the man to do. His perception of a circle is a constantly curving line without corners that returns to its origin. As we have said, he cannot see all of the circle at once; he can only see the side facing him. The only way he could see a whole circle would be to get inside it. If he were to draw a circle around himself, though, he could never get out. People in Flatland can accidentally kill themselves by drawing circles around themselves from which they cannot get out. In our three-dimensional world, it would be like accidentally locking yourself in an abandoned refrigerator.

As a result, it takes the man a long time to draw the circle. The sphere is very impatient because he could have done it much faster. Finally, the circle is completed, and the sphere says, "It's about time. Now I want you to rotate the circle."

What he has in mind is for the man in Flatland to rotate the circle perpendicular to the paper, in the third dimension. But what the man in Flatland does, instead, is rotate the circumference of the circle, spinning it like a record/CD on a player.

"No, no! Rotate it the other way, in a third dimension perpendicular to your floor," says the sphere.

"I don't understand!" cries the man in Flatland. "There is no such thing as a 'third dimension,'" and for him this is true. There is no such thing as an up and down in a thickness direction and absolutely no way for him to comprehend what the sphere is talking about or, for that matter, even what the sphere is. The only reality he can understand is the world or dimensions in which he lives. The only way he can comprehend the sphere is in understanding the properties of the sphere as they appear in his dimension—in the paper.

Application to God

The reason I have told you this story is to provide us with a foundation upon which we can build a better understanding of God. When we read statements like, "In the beginning God created the heavens and the earth" (Genesis 1:1), we are reading a description analogous to Flatland. The concept is that God is a being who exists in a higher dimension than we do. We can only understand the properties of God as they appear in our dimension—our limited three-dimensional world.

The Person of God

God has the same kind of relationship to us as the sphere had to Flatland. He touched our little "Flatland," so to speak, and in violation of all of our laws of science, created matter out of nothing other than pure energy. Being in a higher dimension makes God so superior to us that what is natural and ordinary for him is miraculous to us. Not all religions or religious people have this concept of God, but the Bible recognizes this insightful concept and uses it in every single description of God. Notice how God is described:

> God is light (1 John 1:5).
>
> God is love (1 John 4:8, 16).
>
> God is a spirit (John 4:24).
>
> God is not flesh and blood (Matthew 16:17).
>
> God is not a man (Numbers 23:19).
>
> God is the word (John 1:1).
>
> God is unseen (1 John 4:12).

We are frequently confronted with material things we cannot detect in a direct way, yet despite this, we have learned a great deal about them. For example, we have learned much about atoms, photons, electrons, neutrinos, and other subatomic particles by indirectly discovering many of their physical properties.

Knowing an electron's charge, spin, mass, and speed (all of which can be measured indirectly), gives us a workable, though not absolute, picture of what the electron is like. By understanding such properties, we have been able to harness the power of atoms to build atomic bombs, electrons to make television sets, and photons to build lasers.

Likewise, knowing the power of God can be derived from knowing and appreciating his properties. The Bible is the only book that gives us the properties of God. Words like *love*, *spirit*, *patience*, *goodness*, and *justice* describe properties of God. The Bible is not vague about God, but is using accepted scientific techniques when it describes to us how he acts and when it delineates his characteristics in terms we can understand.

This description puts the Bible on the cutting edge of modern-day physics. The current, widely held theory says that for the universe to have come into existence, at least seven other dimensions must exist beyond the four dimensions of length, width, height, and time. Mathematicians have predicted these eleven spacial dimensions in order to unify the four fundamental forces in what they call the Grand Unified Theory (GUT). Since the God who created the universe must exist outside its boundaries, he would have to occupy at least a twelfth dimension. The following biblical texts clearly acknowledge this extra-dimensional characteristic of God.

From the beginning, God has been invisible (1 Timothy 1:17) and has forbidden humans to make any kind of image of him (Deuteronomy 5:8–9). No man can see him and live, we are told (Exodus 33:20). He is not made of flesh (Acts 17:22–29); he is light (Isaiah 60:19); he is love (1 John 4:8). We dwell in him (Acts 17:28), and he lives in our hearts (Romans 8:11), having unlimited time (2 Peter 3:8) to hear every prayer ascending to his throne (2 Chronicles 30:27).

In harmony with our laws of science, he created matter out of pure energy (Hebrews 11:3). He is also unlike anything or anyone we humans can relate to because he is a compound being. He has revealed himself to us in three separate, coexisting persons, yet he is only one God. And perhaps most difficult for any finite person to grasp, he had no beginning and will have no end (Psalm 90:2).

This last scripture in Psalm 90:2 becomes clearer when we adjust our perspective. From the perspective of humans, the God of the Bible has always existed. If God created time and brought it into our universe from another dimension, then he existed before time. In the absence of time, a "beginning" and an "end" are superfluous.

Metaphors for God

The descriptions of God from Genesis to Revelation are totally nonphysical and non-anthropomorphic (not like man). It is true that when we are being told how God acts, sometimes we do see anthropomorphic terms used, like "the hand of God" or "the face of God." But these terms are being used in the same way that we might speak of the "long arm of the law" or the "face of America." Biblical descriptions giving God human characteristics are only metaphors.

For instance, when the book of Daniel (7:9, 13, 22) and the book of Revelation represent God as being ancient, they are calling attention to his agelessness (Psalm 90:2; Revelation 4:9). When God is depicted as having white hair, it is because, in the cultural setting in which the Bible was written, age demanded respect and inspired veneration (Proverbs 20:29). None of these verses is intended to be a literal description of God. The God of the Bible is beyond physical description, and that is why he commanded his followers not to make images of him (Exodus 20:4).

THE DIMENSION OF TIME

We have the same problem as the man in Flatland when we try to comprehend such a complex being as God, especially a Being who never had a beginning. In order to understand this concept a little better, we need to learn some facts about time and how it passes. Have you ever tried to define the word *time*? We have the same conceptual problem with time that we have with God. We cannot see time, smell it, taste it, feel it, or hear it.

Time is like the extra third dimension we considered in our illustration of Flatland. That is why time is said to be a "fourth" dimension because it is an additional measurement component, just like the other three dimensions. However, it does not measure size; it measures location.

In our world, it is physically impossible for two different masses to occupy the same location at the same time. They can occupy the same location at different times, but not at the same time. You and I can both sit on the same chair, but not at the same time, as most of us learned in kindergarten during a game of musical chairs.

Since we can measure our other three dimensions with a ruler and actually "see" them, time becomes very mysterious when described as a fourth dimension. But the fact that we do not perceive time directly through our senses, like seeing or hearing, does not mean that time does not exist. The atheist, like the Russian cosmonaut who refused to accept the existence of God because he could not perceive him through his senses, is not being very consistent. He certainly would not reject time on that basis even though the concept of time involves the same problem of perception.

THE VARIABILITY OF TIME

In 1905, a young patent clerk named Albert Einstein propounded a theory that not only resulted in substantially changing our concept of the physical world, but also gave us a new tool to pry into God's domain. Einstein's assertions had a profound impact on the physical sciences. One part of his work dealt with the variable nature of time and space when considered on the cosmic level.

Einstein proved that time is not fixed, but varies depending upon the speed at which an object or person is traveling. That is why someone who is sent into space at 99.9999% of the speed of light for only 50 years by his watch, could find, when he returned, that 20,000 years had passed on earth (see appendix 5, page 193). Time is no longer viewed as being a fixed, unchanging quantity that goes on and on forever. It is, instead, a variable that can be controlled by outside factors, such as the speed at which an object or a person is moving. This revolutionary concept is no longer considered just a theory.

Example of the Neutron

As proof, let us look at an experiment that has been done with certain subatomic particles. A single neutron, for example, under static conditions can exist for only about eighteen minutes before it disintegrates to form a proton and an electron, plus some antimatter. When accelerated in a particle accelerator to very high speeds, however, the neutron "lives" considerably longer.

Depending upon the accelerated velocity, the neutron's existence or life is prolonged in comparison with our time as predicted by Einstein's theory. This finding validates our example of a person's life being similarly extended if he or she is accelerated to near the velocity of light. Numerous other observable experiments like this one have added credence to Einstein's concept of time, supporting the novel idea that time is not fixed, but can vary or change with circumstances.

Position of God toward Time

What relevance does this scientific reality have regarding our concept of God? One of the things that confused me most about God when I was an atheist was his relationship to time as described in the Bible. We see the statement, "But, beloved, be not ignorant of this one thing, that one day is with the Lord as a thousand years, and a thousand years as one day" (2 Peter 3:8, KJV). Jude speaks of God as existing "before all time" (Jude 1:25, NAS), and Genesis 1:1 boldly says, "In the beginning God created … ."

The Bible describes God as a B eing who relates to time the way we relate to a wall. Just as we can see the beginning of the wall, the end of the wall, and all points in between, so, too, God can see the beginning and end of time and all points or events in between (Isaiah 46:9–10). John Williams has described God as having "all of eternity in which to listen to the last split-second prayer sent up by a pilot as his plane crashes in flames" (1968, 45).

Is such a description of God reasonable? By examining time in the light of Albert Einstein's equations, we can see that it is. Humans have experimentally shown time to be manipulative, if only to a limited extent. So if humans can slow time even slightly, could not God manipulate it more fully? Since God is the Creator of time, can we not expect him to know a great deal more about it than we do? Absolutely, especially since the inspired biblical description of God's relationship to time has proved to be scientifically rational.

THE PRINCIPLE OF EQUIVALENCE

In Our Dimension

A second part of Einstein's work can verify the nature of God in another way. The principle of equivalence maintains that time and space are inseparably linked. If I ask you how far it is from Chicago to Indianapolis, you might say 180 miles, or you might say three hours. You are measuring by geometric methods in one case and by relative time in the other. Both are valid.

Let me illustrate it to you another way. Suppose I could wave a magic wand and stop time, but you could continue to function in a normal way. Think of what you could do! You could get into your car and drive all the way across the country without any time passing. That would mean that you would be there and here—in both places—at the same time.

If you could stop time, there would be no limit to what you could accomplish. What is it that keeps you from doing everything you want to do? It is time, is it not? How often have you said, "If only I had time, I'd do … ." Time limits how much space we can cover or, in other words, how much we can actually achieve with our lives.

In God's Dimension

If we apply this time/space framework to God, an amazing biblical concept emerges. Since God is not restricted in any way by time, then he must also be unbounded in space. Every point in space must be "here and now" for God. The Bible has consistently upheld this view. In Jeremiah 23:23–24, we read, "'Am I only a God nearby,' declares the LORD, 'and not a God far away? … Do I not fill heaven and earth?' declares the LORD."

What is Jeremiah saying in this passage? That God is here and there and everywhere—all places—at the same time. That is why we refer to God as being "omnipresent." This biblical insight, therefore, is totally consistent with the best scientific evidence we have confirming the relationship between time and space. The idea that "In him we live and move and have our being" (Acts 17:28) fits such a concept, as do all of the biblical references to the relationship of God to time and space (see also Psalm 139).

Understanding this aspect of God allows us to answer a myriad of questions about him. Obviously references to God's skin color, his sex, or any other physical characteristic are no longer relevant. We are not dealing with a God who has any three-dimensional human need or weakness. He has all the best characteristics of all races and sexes and is deficient in nothing.

God cannot die, because death is dependent upon time. If time does not pass for God, death is impossible. God had no beginning because beginning by definition implies time. Since he existed before time began, he has always been. Therefore, he can speak of events that took place before time began (1 Corinthians 2:7; Titus 1:2; Jude 25). This is why only God and Jesus can say, "I am the Alpha and the Omega, … the Beginning and the End" (Revelation 22:13).

We call this timeless state *eternity*. Eternity is not how long it would take an ant to move Mount Everest, grain by grain, from Los Angeles to New York and back again. Eternity is not how long a lecture or a sermon is, though sometimes it may seem that way. Eternity is that higher order or dimension where time does not exist at all!

If time does not exist, then all of the negative things that go along with time would not exist either. There would be no more death, pain, tears, or crying, because all these things are related to our time-bound, three-dimensional world. Revelation 21:1 gives precisely this description of what will happen at the end of time, calling this higher dimension or domain a "new heaven and a new earth."

The God who created both heaven and earth invites us to learn even more about him through studying the natural world around us.

> But ask the animals, and they will teach you, or the birds of the air, and they will tell you; or speak to the earth, and it will teach you, or let the fish of the sea inform you. Which of all these does not know that the hand of the LORD has done this? (Job 12:7–9)

We have seen that there is strong scientific support for the fact that the creation had a beginning. We have seen that the beginning had to be caused because self existence is not a scientific option if there was a beginning. We have seen that the beginning was not caused by chance or an agent that relies totally on chance — that intelligence, purpose, and design are properties of the agent that caused the beginning. We have also seen that the nature of that cause had to be an entity outside of three-dimensional space and independent of time. Various names have been applied to that entity, but the next question we need to ask is whether any one concept of it is any better than any other? If we have rejected naturalism and chance as the causal agents of the creation process does it automatically have to be the God of the Bible?

There are many ways of answering this question. All religious books have beauty, usefulness, and at least some elements of Truth. Is the statement of Jesus that "I am the way and the truth and the life. No one comes to the Father except through me," (John 14:6) just an arrogant claim of superiority, or is there evidence that in fact the Bible is the exclusive Word of God and that it is what we should follow in our spiritual quests?

Chapter 6

WHY CHOOSE THE BIBLE AS THE WORD OF GOD?

In my own case, when I finally left atheism and accepted the existence of God, I began a spiritual quest to determine who God was and what he expected of me. My reading included the Vedas, Upanishads, the Bhagavad-Gita, the Koran, Tripitaka, Avesta, Tao Te Ching, Angas, Upangas, Bab, Bahá'u'lláh, and even the Book of Mormon. Since becoming a Christian, I have reread some of these books, especially the Koran, to make more specific comparisons with the Bible.

All holy books are interesting and beautiful in their own way. The authors present attractive ideas and, through the application of common sense, agree on many of the basic issues. Therefore, the question becomes not whether these words are wise, well-written, or beautiful, but whether they actually represent the word of the God who created the universe. When choosing a book for spiritual guidance, it must be complete and correct in all aspects; otherwise, it could never have any significant impact on a person's life or be depended upon to help in making important decisions.

What evidence do we have showing that the Bible alone is the only reliable source of pure truth? Why should it be used exclusively for spiritual guidance to the exclusion of all the other sources I have mentioned?

INTERNAL EVIDENCE
Simplicity and Clarity

Within the pages of the Bible, we find a simplicity and a clarity conspicuously missing from other contemporaneous works of literature. When I was assigned to read Homer's *Iliad* in high school, I found myself more confused than informed. I remember complaining to my English teacher about her selection of study material. Her response was that since the *Iliad* was written around 800 B.C., I should not expect it to make as much sense as something written more recently. At that time, people had a vastly different world-view, often a much more indirect way of reasoning, and a wordier style of expression than we use today. Thus, it is often very difficult for someone living now to readily grasp the literal meaning expressed by ancient writers.

On the other hand, notice the simplicity of the first statement in the Bible: "In the beginning God created the heavens and the earth." As I have previously stated, I have a mentally-retarded son who has an intelligent quotient (IQ) of about 55. He can read that passage and understand it. The scriptural passage we are talking about was probably written some 700 years before the date of the *Iliad*, yet it is easily understood today.

In addition to simplicity of style, the Bible contains remarkable clarity. A verse-by-verse comparison with the Vedas will convince the reader of how sharp a contrast there is between these two books. A Hindu friend of mine confided to me that although he held a Ph.D. and was an upper-caste Hindu, he could not understand the Vedas and neither could any of his peers. If you question the validity of that statement, I urge you to secure a copy and read it for yourself. You will soon discover that the Bible is unique in its clarity.

Confident Voice

Another characteristic of the Bible is the obvious confidence with which its writers spoke and wrote. In contrast, writers of other holy books often express personal insecurity by interjecting such qualifiers as "I swear this is true" or "I am positive this is right." Yet nowhere in the writings of the Bible or in the message of Jesus

Christ do we encounter comparable adjurations. Rather, people said of Jesus, "No one ever spoke the way this man does" (John 7:46), "because he taught as one who had authority, and not as their teachers of the law" (Matthew 7:29).

On another occasion, Jesus specifically discouraged prodigious oaths by saying,

> But I tell you, Do not swear at all: either by heaven, for it is God's throne; or by the earth, for it is his footstool; or by Jerusalem, for it is the city of the Great King. And do not swear by your head, for you cannot make even one hair white or black. Simply let your "Yes" be "Yes," and your "No," "No"; anything beyond this comes from the evil one (Matthew 5:34–37).

This simple, straightforward recommendation contrasts significantly with the Koran, where we see hundreds of expressions of insecurity, such as "By Allah, I swear this is true."

Brevity

When historians or storytellers write and politicians or preachers speak, they are seldom brief. Conversely, the Bible is simple and to the point, especially in the Old Testament Genesis account of creation and in the New Testament style of writing in general.

For instance, in any large library in this country, there are millions of volumes of scientific material dealing with the origin of the universe and life. Dr. Carl Sagan estimated that there may be as many as 40 million books written about this subject. All of these 40 million volumes of scientific material are implicitly summarized in the first 31 verses of the Bible.

Paradoxically, this straightforward simplicity is also one of the problems that some people have with the Genesis record. They expect to find the essential knowledge of all those 40 million volumes somehow stated explicitly within these 31 short verses. While such an excess of information might satisfy some modern-day critics, it certainly would have been of no benefit to the great majority of the readers of Genesis. So the way the Bible has managed to convey

God's creation message with simple but scientifically sound word-images is nothing short of miraculous.

Additional examples of brevity abound in the Bible. The baptism of Jesus is adequately reported using only four verses. The transfiguration of Christ, which is certainly a momentous event, is covered in only five verses, excluding his journey up and down the mountain. Of the 12,000 days that Jesus Christ dwelt on the earth and of the 1,200 days of his active ministry, only about 34 total days are accounted for in the Bible.

I had a friend who studied biographical styles for his doctoral thesis. One biography of John F. Kennedy that he reviewed included 183 more days in Kennedy's life than he had lived! Not so in the Bible. All unnecessary data are omitted.

Although brevity is appealing to the reader, it sometimes imposed a challenge to the Bible writers. We can almost sense their frustration because it seems as if they were not allowed to write as much as they would have liked. John says things like "Even the world itself could not contain the books" that he would like to have written (John 21:25, KJV). This unusual economy of words is not typical of other religious books. Just the sheer size of the Vedas literally proves this point. In the Koran, we see numerous examples of unnecessary detail, such as how many times a day Muhammad brushed his teeth.

Fulfilled Prophecy

While the account of Jesus' ministry may have been brief, it was, nevertheless, complete enough to establish the Bible as the indisputable Word of God. Writing history in advance or prophesying with absolute accuracy is something only God can do. In harmony with this, we find that Jesus' ministry was preceded by several hundred prophecies, which served to establish, beyond a reasonable doubt, that he was the true son of God.

Dr. Peter Stoner, Professor Emeritus of Science at Westmont College, decided to assign his graduate students the task of calculating what the odds would be for these events to have happened by chance. Using just the first eight of the prophecies listed in the shaded box titled "Prophecies Concerning the Messiah," he calculated that the odds would be 1 in 10^{17} (that is, 1 in 100,000,000,000,000,000).

According to reliable sources, Dr. Stoner's calculations have been reviewed and verified by a committee of the American Scientific Affiliation, Goshen College, and by the Executive Council of that same group ("Prophecies Concerning the Messiah" 2000).

Since this figure greatly exceeds the number of people who have ever lived, it can be safe to assume that it would be impossible for

Prophecies Concerning the Messiah

1. *Where he would be born (Micah 5:2; Matthew 2:1).*
2. *He would be preceded by a messenger (Isaiah 40:3; Matthew 3:3).*
3. *How he would enter Jerusalem (Zechariah 9:9; Matthew 21:4–11).*
4. *His friends would betray him (Psalm 41:9; Matthew 10:4).*
5. *He would be betrayed for thirty pieces of silver (Zechariah 11:12; Matthew 26:15).*
6. *How the betrayal money would be used (Zechariah 11:13b; Matthew 26:15; 27:7).*
7. *He would be silent before his accusers (Isaiah 53:7; Matthew 27:11–14).*
8. *His hands and feet would be pierced (Psalm 22:16; Matthew 27:35; John 20:25).*
9. *He would suffer and redeem us (Isaiah 53:5–6, 11–12; Romans 5:17–18).*
10. *He would be beaten and spit upon (Isaiah 50:6; Matthew 26:67).*
11. *He would be given gall and vinegar to drink (Psalm 69:21; Matthew 27:34).*
12. *His clothing would be divided by lots (Psalm 22:18; Matthew 27:35).*
13. *He would cry out (Psalm 22:1; Matthew 27:46).*
14. *Darkness would cover the land (Amos 8:9; Matthew 27:45).*
15. *He would be buried with the rich (Isaiah 53:9; Matthew 27:57–60).*
16. *He would be called God (Isaiah 9:6; John 20:28).*

these events to have happened by chance alone. Some may argue that Jesus intentionally set out to fulfill personal prophecies, which would slightly bias the odds in his favor. While that is possible in some instances, there is a significant number of predictions over which he had no control, such as his lineage, his birthplace, and his mother's circumstances, to name just a few. These more than offset those he could have deliberately fulfilled, clearly showing that the supernatural was involved.

Honesty

In addition to the features we have listed, freedom from whitewash is another important characteristic of the Bible. The normal procedure to follow when writing a book of praise about someone is to omit any negative comments. For example, after reading the biography of John F. Kennedy, I came away feeling that this man had lived a flawless life. In recent years, however, other writings have shown that President Kennedy had some serious weaknesses that were not exposed in the biography I read.

In the Bible, we do not see this kind of whitewash. When we read about Abraham, who is truly one of the great heroes of the Old Testament, we also read about his weaknesses. We see him willing to allow his wife to become a part of a ruler's harem on two different occasions because Abraham did not really trust in God. Then we read about David, who is said to be a man after God's own heart, and his sins are not hidden from our view. We are informed that he not only committed adultery with the wife of one of his best soldiers, but he also became an accessory to murder in order to suppress the truth of his affair. This information is not flattering to David, and it certainly is not what a nation would want history to record about its greatest hero. Nonetheless, the story is there and is spelled out in all its appalling details.

Such honesty is proof of the Bible's inspiration. If the Bible had been solely the product of human effort, these sordid accounts would no doubt have been excluded. This type of candor cannot be attributed to the Koran. It contains a group of selected quotes by Muhammad written by his contemporaries. When assembling it, the compilers chose to include only the best and the wisest of Muhammad's sayings and to exclude everything else.

CHECKABILITY

By checkability, we refer to statements in the Bible that can be checked to see whether or not they are accurate. One feature of the Bible that makes it easily verifiable is the language in which it was written. Adding to its simplicity and clarity of style is the vernacular of the people who wrote it. Common, concrete nouns and clear action verbs are easily translated into modern languages with no essential loss of meaning. For those words and phrases that are ambiguous, the reader does not have to be a Hebrew or Greek scholar to understand them. All key words can be found in Hebrew or Greek lexicons.

Even though translators of the original Hebrew, Aramaic, and Greek have been careful in their translations, human errors have crept in from time to time, as well as differences based upon the interpretations and opinions of the translators. Sometimes limited knowledge of the original languages has caused confusion, such as whether Jonah was swallowed by a whale or a big fish. Other times, numerical data are poorly interpreted, which may require a detailed study to explain an apparent variance in the account.

However, these errors and problems are minor and are of little significance. They do not negate the claim that the original manuscripts of the Bible were literally inspired by God and thus were error free. In other words, we are asserting that the Bible is the inerrant Word of God.

If this is true, then it will not contain gross errors reflecting the ignorance of the men who wrote it. While the Bible does not specifically address scientific issues, it should not be filled with many of the local superstitious fantasies characteristic of the day in which it was written. What we should find are statements that are too insightful and profound to be attributed to luck or to advanced knowledge on the part of some of its human authors. Let us examine a few of the more impressive examples that prove inspiration by God. (See Appendices A and B, pages 161 and 171, respectfully, for more examples.)

The Value of Blood

During George Washington's time and well after his death, the medical practice of bloodletting was carried on. Barbers made a part of their living by bleeding people. The reason for this practice, which was also done in Egypt during the time of Moses, was that doctors believed that disease originated in the blood. To get rid of the disease, one should get rid of the "bad blood." Bloodletting, then, was an essential part of virtually all medical treatment.

Today we realize the foolishness of this practice because over the past 200 years, we have come to understand that blood serves a very useful role in fighting disease. Ironically, humanity could have known the importance of blood 3,200 years ago simply by reading Leviticus 17:1–14. In this passage, Moses, though trained in Egypt and aware of bloodletting, clearly states that blood is necessary for life. Bloodletting was not a teaching of the Hebrew Torah, even though it was taught by the surrounding nations of that day. As a result, Moses' statement about the significance of blood predates modern medical science by about 3,000 years.

Human Reproduction

In ancient Roman mythology, two boys named Romulus and Remus were born out of the mud and later became the founders of the city of Rome. As we can see from this myth, the idea that women were not always necessary when it came to human reproduction has ancient roots. It was believed many centuries ago that males alone possessed the seed of life and females provided nothing more than an ideal environment for the growing seed.

There were civilizations that built their whole social structure and sometimes even their religious beliefs around this concept. The results were that women came to be looked upon as nothing more than a man's property and a measure of his wealth and prestige. A man who collected many wives was a man who was wealthy, for wealth was necessary to support a harem. In some cultural systems, when such a man died, his wives were buried with him, whether they were dead or not.

On the other hand, the biblical view of women is radically different. In Genesis 2:22 – 24, God indicated the importance of women and their very special relationship to men by creating the first woman, Eve, from Adam's rib. Much later, the apostle Paul highlighted the significance of this act by showing that although the first woman came from man, all other men have come from women through the birthing process. So there was no basis for men to feel superior to women from a creation point of view (1 Corinthians 11:11–12).

Even more important is the fact that in Genesis 3:15 (KJV), mention is made of a woman's seed, yet the first egg of a woman (her seed) was not visibly seen until around 1922. The promise made to Eve's seed clearly shows the correctness of the biblical concept of women and their role in the process of human reproduction.

Animal Reproduction

Sometimes a more careful reading of the text substantiates the checkability of the Bible. A case in point is the animal husbandry practiced by Jacob in the book of Genesis. Critics have argued that here the Bible is contaminated by archaic, local folklore. Contrary to this claim, we find that if an account happens to include a description of events that may be founded upon superstition and myth, the biblical text usually clarifies matters with a qualifying statement or explanation.

Genesis 30:37–43 describes how Jacob apparently tried to develop a breed of goats that had spotted or speckled bodies. Critics have used this text to show that Jacob believed he could cause an animal to be born with spots if the mother was shown a spotted object while she was mating. By his actions, it is very likely that Jacob did feel this way and did, in fact, believe that he was successful, because an unusually large number of spotted animals were born to his father-in-laws's flocks at this time.

But rather than endorsing a practice that today we know is false, the Bible shows that Jacob's success was not founded upon his own efforts at breeding goats. A careful reading of Genesis 31:10–12 reveals the actual reason why Jacob prospered: "In breeding season I once had a dream in which I looked up and saw that the male goats mating with the flock were streaked, speckled or spotted. The angel of God said to me in the dream, 'Jacob.' I answered, 'Here I am.'

And he said, 'Look up and see that all the male goats mating with the flock are streaked, speckled or spotted.'"

Here we find that God miraculously increased the libido of the spotted males, which apparently resulted in only spotted offspring. Though initially God allowed Jacob to assume that his success was due to his own personal, unscientific efforts, we later learn that Jacob had nothing to do with it. God was entirely responsible. He was causing *all* "the male goats mating with the flock" to be spotted. Obviously, God inspired this explanation because it was based upon genetics and not upon the primitive breeding methods practiced by Jacob and his contemporaries. Thus we find that the details in this account provide evidence for the checkability of the Bible.

Bacterial Contamination

Moses has been referred to by some writers as the world's first microbiologist. This idea developed because of the wisdom seen in his writings relating to the fields of hygiene, diet, and quarantine. We must remember that even during most of the nineteenth century, knowledge about diseases was so vague that bacterial infection ran rampant. Doctors would perform an autopsy in a hospital morgue, and then, without washing their hands, they would perform surgery, deliver a baby, or conduct a hands-on examination of a patient. The death rate among women giving birth in these hospitals ranged from 25 to 30%.

When Dr. Ignaz Phillip Semmelweis, who was practicing in Vienna, Austria, tried to change this procedure in the 1840s, he was driven into seclusion by his colleagues, in spite of the fact that his insistence upon simple hand washing had been proven effective. In wards under his charge, the death rate of his patients averaged no more than 0.85%. Ironically, Semmelweis died of childbirth fever (puerperal fever), a disease he spent his entire professional life trying to eradicate. He apparently caught the disease from one of his infected patients.

Is it a coincidence that 3,200 years ago, a man who knew nothing about bacteria, infection, or any of our modern medical concepts gave us a system of hygiene that is still followed by doctors today? Let us examine some of the rules given by Moses to the Israelites that we now know to be bacteriologically sound.

Handling Dead Objects

In Numbers 19:5–22 and Leviticus 13–15, Moses commands that an individual touching a dead person or animal should be quarantined. Prescribed washings and the burning of the clothes of one who contacted a dead person are given in the same passages. Even a casual observer can see the wisdom behind these commands. Any animal or person who died of unknown causes is likely to have died of a communicable disease.

The prescribed washings, burnings, and isolations Moses required would help to avoid the epidemic normally spread by such a bacterial or viral agent. The beneficial effect of these procedures became obvious when those who did not follow God's commands frequently became sick. Eventually this led people to erroneously associate sickness in general with sinfulness, which is why Jesus' disciples asked him, "Rabbi, who sinned, this man or his parents, that he should be born blind?" (John 9:2, NAS).

Burying Wastes and Quarantine

In Europe during the Dark Ages, people threw their waste products out the window into the street. The stench and pollution problems were bad enough, but even more important were the infection and disease problems caused by such a careless waste-disposal system. Writers of the time record that flies, rats, and other disease-carrying organisms thrived in the garbage found in the streets. The black plague, encephalitis epidemics, and a variety of other scourges have been attributed to this waste-disposal practice.

These facts make us appreciate even more the words in Deuteronomy 23:12–14, where Moses commands the Israelites to bury their wastes. Additionally, a person having any kind of discharge from his or her body was isolated or quarantined from the rest of the people. Even such bodily functions as menstruation and ejaculation were put into this unclean category. While this may have seemed extreme to us in the past, now because of the HIV virus (AIDS epidemic), we can readily appreciate the importance of removing all possible sources of disease. Yet during the time of Moses and for 3,000 years afterward, the whole concept of unseen contamination was totally foreign to human thought. Clearly, Moses had supernatural help in deriving his medical directives.

Prohibiting Certain Foods

Methods for cooking food during the time of Moses were highly inadequate, to say the least. The wandering Israelite population did not possess efficient ovens, nor did they have any way of refrigerating their foods as we do today. It should be obvious, then, that certain types of foods that could contain hard-to-kill parasites, worms, and bacteria would need to be avoided. In Leviticus 11, we observe that Moses excluded those very items from the Israelites' diet by forbidding pork, the flesh of scavengers like vultures, and many other potentially dangerous food sources. He even forbade the eating of animal blood (Leviticus 17:12–14), which is still done by some cultures despite the bacteriological hazards involved.

We are just now understanding the reasons for many of these dietary restrictions, like the avoidance of eating fat (Leviticus 3:17; 7:23). Moses' uncanny accuracy in singling out so-called clean and unclean animals goes beyond any chance logic. It is another clear demonstration of the miraculous source of his writings.

We can now see that these health commands by God were an important way of protecting his chosen people from the likelihood of being decimated by infectious disease. This, of course, was absolutely necessary if they were to survive as a nation long enough to provide the right kind of godly community within which Jesus Christ, the Son of God, could be properly raised.

Astronomy

Understandably, in the past, the combination of primitive superstition and a limited observer's viewpoint of the heavens and earth resulted in some fantastic astronomical theories postulated by ancient civilizations. In Hindu writings, the earth is described as resting on the backs of four elephants. The elephants are standing on the back of a giant turtle who is swimming in a sea of milk (Branley and Wimmer 1970, 30–36). Earthquakes, tsunamis (tidal waves), and other upsets in the earth's equilibrium are brought about when an elephant sneezes or tries to scratch itself.

The Japanese taught in many of their religious traditions that the earth was suspended on the back of a giant catfish. Once again, the various cataclysmic events that took place upon the earth could be explained by movements of the fish. Even the scholarly Greek civilization at one point taught that the earth was suspended upon the back of a god named Atlas.

These beliefs stand in sharp contrast to a people who depended upon the one and only God for direction. Moses, who probably wrote Genesis, was trained in Egypt where the sun was worshipped as the god Ra and where the Egyptians, like the surrounding nations, had elaborate observatories and descriptions of star configurations. Yet Moses' writings were entirely free from mythological fantasy as an explanation for the suspension of the earth.

Even though the Bible makes very few remarks about the mechanics of the earth's position in space, the poetic writer of Job makes the statement, "He suspends the earth over nothing" (Job 26:7). The profundity of this ancient statement may not be obvious to us in this technological day of space travel. But when we consider how much astronomy was known 4,000 years ago in Job's day, we should recognize that this statement is without precedent. It was made thousands of years before Isaac Newton was supposedly struck by an apple and proposed the now accepted universal law of gravitation. It was an equally long time before the law of action-reaction was understood or the nature of centrifugal force was perceived, along with its importance in keeping the earth from colliding with the sun or spinning uncontrollably off into outer space.

Therefore, it was only through inspiration by God that Job was able to make such an accurate statement about the suspension of the earth when other ancient scientists spoke in terms of giant elephants, catfish, and a Greek god's shoulders.

PHYSICAL SCIENCE

We have said a number of times that the Bible is not a book of science. For this reason, we want to emphasize that we are not suggesting that the men who wrote these facts intended to be stating ideas relating to science. However, if the Bible is the Word of God, then we would expect it to be accurate. Because of this, when a scientific fact is implied or shown by example, it should be consistent with what we know scientifically today. To prove this hypothesis, let us briefly consider some additional examples where scientific issues are implied. In doing this, we will be impressed with the uniqueness of the subject matter and the difficulty in attributing the wisdom behind the words to the human writer alone.

Scientific Principles

In 1856, Hubert Spencer outlined a new and significant framework for scientific research and writing that gave substance and direction to analytical work. He asserted that in order for a scientific report to be useful, it must include all the relevant elements of the problem, such as time, force, action, or direction, and weight or matter. In this regard, it is interesting to note that the Bible was the first report ever to contain all these vital elements as recognized by Spencer. Notice that Genesis 1:1 says, "In the beginning [time] God [force] created [action] the heavens and the earth [matter]." It seems that the biblical writer knew intuitively the best method of formatting a scientific report. Even though this is a minor point, it emphasizes the Bible's faithfulness to details.

Shipbuilding

It is scripturally significant that the first reinforced concrete ship ever launched had the dimensions 300 x 50 x 30 feet (DeHoff 1959, 53). Modern hydraulic architects have learned that a certain ratio between length, width, and height produces greater seaworthiness than other dimension ratios. These discoveries have come about through a long history of trial-and-error experiments. Even in our modern day of marine engineering and oceanographic technology, the basic size ratio of all ships considered to produce maximum seaworthiness is 30 x 5 x 3.

In Genesis 6:15, we read a 3,200-year-old narrative of God-given instructions to a man who was building a boat that had to be the epitome of seaworthiness. The dimensions of this boat were to be 300 x 50 x 30 cubits (30 x 5 x 3 ratio). Not only were the dimension ratios given accurately, but the ship also had design features that were not incorporated into sailing ships until relatively recent times.

The thin plank hull of Noah's ark was pitched (sealing pitch) instead of being made out of lightweight, bulky materials that could be depended upon to stay afloat by themselves. This was a novel technique for that day and time. It was pitched both inside and out to produce a watertight structure, another feature that was not introduced until much later in history. The below-deck area was compartmentalized into a sort of stateroom division now found on modern ocean liners. This design gives the vessel greater structural integrity.

In the ancient past, materials such as low density logs and marsh reeds were used because of their buoyancy. Noah's ark introduced the water-displacement concept, wherein a watertight box or hull made of strong, dense materials will readily float if it weighs less than the water it displaces. This idea was unique for that day, and it causes us to marvel at another "happy coincidence," scientifically speaking.

Geography/History/Archaeology

When we consider that at least forty different men were involved in writing the Bible over thousands of years, its accuracy geographically, historically, and archaeologically is amazing. When the Bible says a certain man went up or down from a certain place going to another place, geographic references have been correct in every testable case. The Bible is also accurate historically. Archaeologists and historians recognize that the Bible furnishes tremendous insights into the history of the period in which it was written. Even those records in the Bible thought to be in error (such as the existence of the Hittite nation that critics disclaimed for many years to be a biblical myth) have been shown by archaeologists to be true. It is not surprising that the official publication of the The American Schools of Oriental Research (ASOR) is called the *Biblical Archaeologist* (since late 1997 it has been called *Near Eastern Archaeology*). In its very interesting quarterly reports, it testifies again and again to the accuracy of biblical accounts.

MORALITY

Today a humanistic society, strongly influenced by evolutionary concepts, is trying to promote selfishness in the guise of "freedom." The message is "Do anything you want to. Since this life is all you have, there is no reason to live by an outdated moral code. Get what you can and enjoy it." Friedrich Nietzsche, a famous German philosopher, is reputed to have said, "There is no reason why the stronger and smarter should continue to be constrained by a 'value' that is obviously not in their interest" (Grant 1988).

As Individuals

In stark contrast with this self-centered philosophy, Jesus tells us how to live successfully by showing concern for others and by controlling our minds and thoughts. In Matthew chapters 5 and 6, not only are we told not to commit adultery, but we are told to keep such thoughts out of our minds altogether. Not only are we told not to murder, but we are told not to hate either.

The Bible makes an encouraging promise in 1 Corinthians 10:13: "No temptation has seized you except what is common to man. And God is faithful; he will not let you be tempted beyond what you can bear. But when you are tempted, he will also provide a way out so that you can stand up under it."

Those Christians who have believed and lived according to this promise can testify to its fulfillment in their lives.

Within the Family

The Bible also tells us how to deal with our home life intelligently and rationally. In Mark 10:6–9, Jesus commands that all men should practice a monogamous marriage relationship — one husband, one wife — for life. In fact, Jesus alludes to Genesis 2:24, which indicates that this was God's will from the very beginning. The alternative to this command is polygamy (multiple wives) and polyandry (multiple husbands). If you are a woman, do you really believe you can have the kind of relationship you want in life with a man who is also married to other women? Or if you are a man, do you really believe you can have what you want out of a marriage if you have to share your wife with other men? There is no question about the practicality and wisdom of the marriage requirements given in the Bible. This arrangement was intended to give children both a father and a mother devoted to raising them in a secure, loving family environment. Wherever this system has been followed, coupled with godly works, it has resulted in happy, well-adjusted individuals.

Within the Community

Assuming that our home life is in order, how are we to deal with people outside the home? The Bible tells us that we are to love other people, to be willing to symbolically turn the other cheek to them in times of conflict, and not to return evil for evil. In Matthew 5:41, the writer tells us that if a person is compelled to go one mile, he should go two miles.

In Roman times, it was law that a Roman soldier could require any Jewish citizen to carry his load for up to one mile, which was exactly 1,000 paces (1,620 yards). However, the involuntary draftee was not required to go one pace beyond the legislated distance. It must have made a favorable impression on a Roman soldier when a Christian would volunteer to carry the load for 2,000 paces.

Implicit in this command from God were several requirements for sound mental health. A person who is forgiving, loving, polite, and free from prejudice is a well-adjusted, successful citizen. Jesus not only recommended this moral way of life, he lived it himself. He proved many times that neither he nor his Father are prejudiced (Acts 10:34–35).

Although Samaritans were shunned and despised by the Jews, Jesus had direct fellowship with several Samaritans, including one woman of questionable reputation. In two passages (Luke 10:30–37 and John 4:3–24), the Samaritans are viewed in a very positive light by Jesus and the Bible writer. In John 4, Jesus deals directly with the Samaritan woman, and she expresses surprise at this. Thus by example and command, Jesus teaches us tolerance and love and appreciation, no matter what our racial, social, or economic circumstance.

What is the alternative to this godly system given to us in the Bible? We would have a system where there is little, if any, motivation toward true unselfishness. Such a system inevitably produces prejudice, bigotry, and anarchy. The Bible does not simply recommend, it motivates people to perform good works. For this reason, the Bible's instruction on how to get along with other people cannot be improved upon. One time when asked what he thought about Christianity in general, Carl Sandburg responded by saying, somewhat wryly, that he did not know—he had never seen it tried yet. Unfortunately, there are many people today who have not seen Christianity tried, even in the lives of some of those who claim to be Christians.

THE AUTHOR

Finally, perhaps the most important reason to choose the Bible as the Word of God has to do with its author. When we examine the other religions in the world, we find that all of the responsibility for establishing a relationship with God falls upon the seeker—humanity must reach up to God. God does not help at all in these religious systems. It is up to each individual to reach the goal—whether the goal is Nirvana or Brahma or whatever it might be. If a person is not capable of reaching the goal using his own strength and merit, then he may have to make repeated attempts by being reincarnated over and over again.

Notice the contrast in the Bible when the angel Gabriel told Mary her son would be called Immanuel, "which means, 'God with us'" (Matthew 1:23). In the last book of the New Testament, the resurrected Jesus says, "Here I am. I stand at the door and knock. If anyone hears my voice and opens the door, I will come in and eat with him, and he with me" (Revelation 3:20).

In John 10:14–18, the relationship of a shepherd with his sheep is given to characterize a personal God, not wanting any of us to be lost, but wanting all of us to be saved and live eternally with him (1 Timothy 2:3–4; 2 Peter 3:9). This reward is so awe-inspiring that it cannot be expressed in words. We are told that there will not be any more pain or suffering or agony (1 Corinthians 15:50–58; Revelation 21:3–4). Our bodies will be changed to live in God's domain forever.

For those who diligently apply the Bible to their lives, there is a freedom from many of the serious problems plaguing this generation. Exhaustive studies have been done to see if being a Christian makes any difference in people's abilities to overcome drugs, alcohol, depression, mental illness, disease, and poverty. The National Institute for Health Care Research has found that Christianity has a statistically significant positive effect on people in general.

There are all sorts of people who demonstrate changed lives-freed from every problem imaginable. Testimony can be a risky road to truth because testimonies are often difficult to document from a scientific perspective. However, there are just too many cases to ignore where people have been turned from pursuing their own selfish schemes to living a life in pursuit of godly works. For an exhaustive discussion of the practical effect of Christianity on mankind we recommend the reader secure Alvin Schmidt's wonderful book, *Under the Influence* (see References for chapter 6, page 227).

So there are many reasons to choose the Bible as the inspired Word of God. We can have complete confidence in a book that is open to scrutiny in all areas of human life and consistently proves to be accurate — scientifically, socially, and religiously. The more we study the Bible, the more convinced we become that not only does God exist, but he personally encourages and rewards those who earnestly seek to know him better (Hebrews 11:6). In our next several chapters we wish to look at some of the hard questions of why God created man, and why there are horrible stories and perceived errors in the Bible — the why questions.

Chapter 7

WHY — IS THERE EVIL?
— DO WE EXIST?
— DO WE SUFFER?

A discussion of reasons to believe in God would not be complete without addressing one of the biggest barriers to the acceptance of an omnipotent Creator—the existence and continued thriving of evil in this world. Understandably, an atheist might argue that even if scientific evidence points toward the existence of God, the injustice, suffering, and pain of this life deny both his power and his love.

Yet in the midst of all this injustice and pain, Christians are able to maintain faith in a God of love. How is this possible? What does the Bible reveal about evil; why we exist; why we experience pain, suffering, and death; and what kind of God is it who would permit all of this.

THE LAW OF PARITY

First, we should recognize that the mere existence of evil does not necessarily mean there is no loving God. The coexistence of good and evil is in harmony with a basic concept in science and philosophy called the law of parity. This law states that for a physical process or form there is a mirror image. We are all familiar with the parity principle and how it helps us understand things. In biology class we came to know about bilateral symmetry which told us that if something has a left eye it is going to have a right eye. We know that if something has a left hand, it will have a right hand. There are occasional exceptions like a flounder or halibut, but the principle works very well in most cases. In psychology we talked about id and ego, which again fit the parity concept in a very good way. In physics the parity principle has led to some strange understandings causing Dr. Carl Anderson in 1932 to look for a particle that would be the mirror image of the negatively charged electron. He hypothesized that a positively charged particle with properties identical to the electron in every way, but opposite, should exist. Based on this law, Dr. Anderson did indeed discover a positively charged electron that, when it touches a normal electron, results in total annihilation.

Dr. Anderson's Nobel Prize-winning discovery of antimatter brings up another possible application of the law of parity, namely that equal amounts of matter and antimatter should exist in space. Could it be, then, that there are galaxies, solar systems, planets, and even some forms of life out there made of positrons, antiprotons, and antineutrons, identical to us in every way but fundamentally opposite? If true, we can imagine a tragic love story involving the matter boy and the antimatter girl whose passion drives them to indulge in one fleeting but fatal kiss, resulting in an enormous nuclear reaction that consumes them both.

Bringing the subject back to reality, we see that the law of parity in the natural world can often result in equal but opposite forces. In the case of matter and antimatter, we are dealing with concrete, measurable particles that physically support the law of parity.

In the philosophical world, however, parity becomes more like a principle that logically requires an abstract concept such as good to have its antithesis in the concept of evil. How can we appreciate the value of being good if we have no comprehension of the negative effects associated with badness? If there is a potential for good, there will also be the potential for the opposite of good, or evil. How did God create good? God *is* good! That is a property of God — a part of his nature.

How, then, did evil come into existence? In the case of evil, God's very existence produces evil. Evil is not a created thing like objects are — evil is a consequence of the existence of good.

Since evil as a mere concept is powerless, it would need to be personified to cause problems. For example, a pornographic book laid on a shelf unread does nothing. Only if someone reads the book and acts upon the information does evil possess any power. So, too, the evil resulting from the existence of good possessed no power until it became personified in a being desiring to oppose God's goodness and love. With this explanation in mind, we can understand how a freewill creature described in the Bible as Satan could exist independently of God's objectives and become the source of evil without God's help or approval (James 1:13). Knowing this, though, is not completely satisfying. It leaves open the question about what kind of relationship Satan has with God. What are our options?

The Concept of Dualism

Some might argue that the principle of parity implies a dualism between God and Satan. If this were true, then Satan would possess all of God's powers in a mirror-image sense. He would be a spiritual being who had always existed and who could oppose God with equal power. He would be able to exist in all places at the same time and could continuously nurture his own selfish interests by miraculously performing evil deeds. Like God, he could create matter from nothing

As far as the Bible is concerned, however, Satan does not have the power necessary to support this concept of dualism. He is described as a spiritual being capable of doing some miraculous things beyond our comprehension, such as his ability to torment Job, but he is not portrayed as the evil equivalent of God. In Job 1 and 2 and in other places throughout the Bible, God effectively limits Satan. Additionally, there is no doubt according to Scripture that God will win out over Satan in the end.

The Description of a Fallen Angel

A preferred alternative to the duality argument is that Satan, the personification of evil, is simply a fallen angel. The Bible describes angels as spiritual beings who have specific assignments of responsibility in God's dimension or what we call heaven (Luke 1:19;

Hebrews 1:14). As "sons of God," they were joyful witnesses when God created our universe (Job 38:7). At one point in the past, the angel referred to as Satan made evil come into tangible existence by revolting against God. As a result, God chose to separate this rebel angel from the rest of his realm by exiling him to the vicinity of the earth, along with those angels who chose to rebel with him.

The following verses support this view:

> For if God did not spare angels when they sinned, but sent them to hell, putting them into gloomy dungeons to be held for judgment … (2 Peter 2:4).

> And the angels who did not keep their positions of authority but abandoned their own home—these he has kept in darkness, bound with everlasting chains for judgment on the great Day (Jude 6).

The above references lend credence to Satan's position as a fallen angel because God clearly exercises superior power over Satan and his agents. So the principle of parity explains why the possibility for evil should exist, and the Bible describes the one who chose to personify it.

We might still wonder, though, what caused Satan to revolt in the first place? Does his fall mean that when humans finally reach heaven, they will still potentially be able to fall victim to evil? Will the practicing of evil never end?

THE NECESSITY OF FREE WILL

To answer these questions, we need to acknowledge the place of free will in God's arrangement. When the Bible speaks of angels "sinning," it appears that God made them with enough free will to choose to be either good or bad. This does not say that God created the evil deeds they perform as a result of their choices any more than God directly causes tragedy in human affairs today. Rather, it means that God only allowed the potential for the expression of evil to exist.

Why would God create intelligent beings with the free will to love or hate? Why would he not just make them so that they could do only good? The answer is that true love is impossible unless there is a choice. If my wife were forced to love me and had no other choice, I could never be really confident of her love. Sexual relations between a man and a woman without choice is called rape and is universally recognized as having nothing to do with love. Real love has to involve a choice. If God's objectives were to include mutual love, then there had to be a choice available for the angels and for us.

By giving his angels the choice to be good or evil, God opened up a potential for revolt. Satan, whose name means "opposer," chose to lead such a revolt and to become the manifestation of evil. In the judgment, those obedient to God will be with him and will experience all the joys associated with love and goodness, whereas the temptation to choose evil will be completely eliminated when the devil and his forces are immobilized forever (Hebrews 2:14–15). At present, Satan apparently rejoices because he is free to show his power by winning over many men and women to support his cause. However, he is also cognizant of his final end, and for this reason, he and his cohorts "believe and tremble" (James 2:19, KJV).

GOD'S PURPOSE IN CREATING HUMANS

The next logical question in this discussion has to do with God's purpose in creating humans. Why did he create us when he knew that our free will could lead us into so much tragedy and pain? What role do we play in the final outcome of God's purpose?

Perhaps we can gain some insight into these questions by reviewing an everyday example. Suppose I have an idea for a machine that I believe is so good that I choose to invest my life's savings to develop it. What would I do to test the idea before committing my resources in such a way?

First, I would create a model of my idea in a lower dimension, such as drawing a plan of the machine on a two-dimensional sheet of paper. We call this drawing a plan or blueprint. Next, I would allow my plan to be examined by a number of critics. I should be prepared to defend my idea, using all my talents to help make it survive any test. If my idea were a good one, it would withstand the test, and then I would have confidence that it would be a worthwhile investment. If the idea were bad, though, it would not pass and probably should be abandoned.

The following biblical passages indicate that our existence and our actions are indeed being observed and tested by critics in heavenly places:

> For our struggle is not against flesh and blood, but against the rulers, against the authorities, against the powers of this dark world and against the spiritual forces of evil in the heavenly realms (Ephesians 6:12).

> His [God's] intent was that now, through the church, the manifold wisdom of God should be made known to the rulers and authorities in the heavenly realms (Ephesians 3:10).

> "Simon, Simon, Satan has asked to sift you as wheat. But I have prayed for you, Simon, that your faith may not fail" (Luke 22:31–32).

God could destroy Satan just as I could shoot the critic of my idea with a gun, but would that give onlookers (spiritual forces in high places) any confidence in either the creation or the Creator? Or would eliminating critics simply support the evil contention that "might makes right?" We are told in the Bible that humans are created a little lower than the angels (Psalm 8:5; Job 1–2). We are also told that after we die, we will become as angels (Mark 12:25). Therefore, humans appear to be the preliminary stage for achieving God's purpose, which is to share his existence eternally with perfect beings created in his image.

Job's Example

While we may not fully understand all of God's plans, we can see, to a limited extent in the book of Job, how God handles some of the issues regarding our existence. In Job 1:8–12, good and evil are personified in God and Satan as they exchange challenges. God holds up Job as an example to show that because Satan's tools of evil do not work on everyone, Satan is not in total control of the earth. Satan accuses God of making Job's existence so comfortable that God has essentially bribed Job into being good. God responds by telling Satan that he will reduce his protection of Job and allow Satan to do anything except harm him bodily.

It is important to point out here that God does not personally attack Job. God does not directly tempt anyone (James 1:13). Instead, he allows humans to deal with the problems necessarily inherent in the exercise of free will, knowing that these problems will only exist temporarily until the achievement of his final objective. At present, our pain is a source of much grief to both God and us.

Most of us are familiar with Job's success in enduring the initial trials and tribulations to which Satan subjected him. Faced with failure in this first attack, Satan confronts God again (Job 2:1–6). He concedes to a mild defeat but claims that if he can cause Job to suffer physical pain, evil will easily triumph.

In response, God allows Satan to afflict Job with severe illnesses. At first, Job reacts with tears, anger, and regret that he had been born. His reaction, in part, was due to ignorance of the cosmic challenge behind his suffering, a challenge that involved the universal issues of free will and of God's eternal, loving purpose for his human children.

We might read about Job and conclude that while God did not cause Job's suffering, he was indirectly cruel and unloving in allowing it to happen. Yet this experience, as bad as it was, eventually opened Job's eyes with regard to God's majesty and power. He was assured that the all-powerful Creator of heaven and earth was aware of his suffering and cared. Even though Job did not receive specific explanations for his misfortunes, he was satisfied that God was in charge and that, from Job's position in time and space, the answers were beyond human comprehension. Therefore, Job finally said to God, "I know that you can do all things; no plan of yours can be thwarted. You asked, 'Who is this that obscures my counsel without knowledge?' Surely I spoke of things I did not understand, things too wonderful for me to know. ... My ears had heard of you but now my eyes have seen you" (Job 42:2–3, 5).

God, in turn, rewarded Job for his faithfulness, just as he promises to reward us for ours.

Our Example

If we accept the account of Job as both factual and as a metaphor for the suffering of humanity, then each of us can replace Job's name with our own. We are all afflicted by Satan, this world, and the consequences of our free will. Therefore, we all need to decide how we should react to the struggle between good and evil. Yet maintaining faith in a God of love is easier for us than it was for Job.

We have the advantage of being aware of the universal issue involved in the attack on Job. We also know more about God's love for us because we have the record of the life and death of Jesus Christ to assure us that God cares. In Christ, even though we do not have all the answers, our need for justice is satisfied.

Christ became the archetypical figure for whom all humanity longs—the disguised king who lives as one of his subjects in order to become a more compassionate king; the general who eats, sleeps, and endures the deprivations of war side by side with his troops before he leads them into battle. In Christ, we see the God who willingly gave up all his advantages to live our life and feel our pain. As Dorothy Sayers expressed it:

> For whatever reason God chose to make man as he is—limited and suffering and subject to sorrows and death—He had the honesty and courage to take His own medicine. Whatever game He is playing with His creation, He has kept His own rules and played fair. He can exact nothing from man that He has not exacted from Himself. He has Himself gone through the whole of human experience, from the trivial irritations of family life and the cramping restrictions of hard work and lack of money to the worst horrors of pain and humiliation, defeat, despair, and death. When He was a man, He played the man. He was born in poverty and died in disgrace and thought it well worthwhile (1969, 14).

I have had some things happen in my life that I do not like. I had a son born blind, mentally retarded, with cerebral palsy and muscular dystrophy. I do not like the fact that I have had that problem to deal with for over 40 years now. I missed many of the joys of having a son because of the constant battle to work with my son so that he could have as high a standard of life as possible. My wife of 49 years died after 60 years of type 1 insulin-dependent diabetes, and the pain of her loss had pushed me to despair over and over.

Though, like Job, we do not have all the answers now, we can be assured that God sympathizes with our fears and will eventually reward our trust in him. He has promised us eternal life in a higher dimension free of suffering and pain in accord with his original plan (Isaiah 25:8; Matthew 25:34; Revelation 21:4). Yes, our pain is real, but when contrasted with eternity, our present life is incredibly short. A whole lifetime of pain can be likened to a trip to the dentist. We get a shot of novocaine or something similar before the dentist works on our teeth. Why? Because we are gladly willing to endure thirty seconds of the needle against what seems like an eternity of drilling. By comparison, how much will seventy-five years of pain and suffering mean in the context of an eternity in God's domain?

What answer would I have to the loss of my wife and the problems of my son if I was still an atheist? How does the atheist deal with the realities of life if this life is all he has and survival of the fittest is the guiding force behind his decisions? Atheists can criticize God because they do not want to be in the role they are in, but all the foot stomping and complaining they can muster does not provide any help in the battle we all face.

The choices we make now will have eternal significance. None of us can be neutral in this matter. If we choose evil, we will experience the consequences associated with that choice. If we choose good, the beauty of God will shine through us now in this world as well as in the world to come, when God's plan will be vindicated and evil will be a thing of the past.

Chapter 8

WHAT ABOUT ALL THOSE MISTAKES IN THE BIBLE?

We have suggested that evidence compels a person to believe that Christianity is different than the other religious systems that exist upon the earth, and that the Bible has scientific credibility in how it approaches the question of creation, the nature of God, and why we exist. Atheists will be quick to respond to such claims by claiming that the Bible is so full of mistakes, and God is shown as such a malevolent character that no thinking person would want to be a Christian. Richard Dawkins says it this way:

> God ... is arguably the most unpleasant character in all of fiction: jealous and proud of it; a petty, unjust, unforgiving control freak; a vindictive, bloodthirsty ethnic cleanser; a misogynistic, homophobic, racist, infanticidal, genocidal, filicidal, pestilential, megalomaniacal, sadomasochistic, ca-priciously malevolent bully (Dawkins, 31).

When I was an atheist I made similar statements to these. My knowledge of the Bible was nonexistent, and my understanding of the times and conditions under which the Bible was written was badly distorted by my prejudices. It is interesting that after Dawkins wrote his diatribe and the rest of his vitriolic attack on the Christian system in a book titled *The God Delusion*, Alister McGrath wrote a book titled *The Dawkins Delusion* that demonstrated Dawkins' prejudice and ignorance so profoundly that one well-known atheist was quoted as saying Dawkins made him ashamed to be an atheist.

> "*The God Delusion* makes me embarrassed to be an atheist, and the McGraths show why." —Michael Ruse, Lucyle T. Werkmeister Professor of Philosophy, and Director of the Program in the History and Philosophy of Science, Department of Philosophy, Florida State University (an endorsement from the cover of *The Dawkins Delusion*.

When an error is claimed to exist in the Bible or a teaching is claimed to be in error there are usually six causes or misunderstandings that have caused the alleged errors

1. THE CLAIMED MISTAKE IS A CULTURAL ISSUE.

Many times two statements are made in the Bible that appear to contradict each other when in reality there is simply a difference in the way the culture reported something. An obvious example is that the hour in which Jesus was crucified is reported by Mark in Mark 15:25 to be the third hour (9:00 A.M.), but reported by John in John 19:14 to be the sixth hour (6:00 A.M.). The apparent conflict is caused because Mark was using the Jewish system of measuring a day (which began at 6:00 P.M. the previous day) and John was using the Roman system which began at 12:00 A.M (midnight). John was recording when Pilate agreed that the Jews could crucify Jesus, whereas Mark was recording when the crucifixion actually took place.

Another example is when the age of Methuselah is reported to be 969 years in Genesis 5:27. It is very likely that these are not Gregorian years. (Which is our calendar established by Pope Gregory XIII in A.D. 1582.) Many early civilizations recorded ages of their notable people in large numbers, but we have not discovered the way to interpret these ages. Just because we do not understand the age system, does not mean every thing back then is wrong. These large biblical ages seem strange, but that does not mean they are incorrect. In many current civilizations ages are measured from different starting points. In China a person's age is measured from conception. In some African countries age is measured from the time the person becomes an adult—the first menstrual cycle in a woman, or when the man proves himself as a man.

A classic example of this problem is in the genealogies in Matthew compared to the same genealogies in Luke. In Matthew 1:17ff the number of generations given from Abraham to Christ is 42. In Luke 3:23–38 the same genealogy is given in 57 generations. Matthew was a Jew writing an account for a Jewish audience, and to them numbers which are multiples of seven were a symbolic structure that the Jews understood. To do that, major characters are left out of the genealogy, such as Joab and Jehoikim. Luke is a Greek writing to a Greek audience. He certainly would not use a Jewish system in writing for Greeks, so unlike Matthew he includes most if not all of the characters of the sequence, not worrying about whether his numbers were multiples of seven. Many claimed conflicts in the Bible fall into this kind of situation and require some study.

Another kind of cultural problem involves practices that may have been necessary at an earlier time in man's history but are not necessary today. Slavery is an example. Jesus Christ taught strongly against slavery and the letters of Paul strongly urge Christians to grow out of slavery. The fact is however, that slavery was not specifically condemned by God or the early church or church leaders. In Philemon Paul encouraged Philemon to allow an escaped slave to return without punishment.

Slavery today is inexcusable. In the time of Moses however, survival was a hand to mouth proposition and when civil strife and war took place people frequently could only survive by becoming slaves. A slave became a part of the household and was cared for and looked after. In 2 Kings 5 a Syrian named Naaman has an Israelite slave girl, and when the Syrian becomes leprous the slave girl expresses concern and proposes a way to get the leprosy cured. She was a functional part of the family. People became slaves in war (Genesis 14:21; Numbers 31:9; Deuteronomy 20:14; 21:10–14), or could be purchased (Genesis 17:12, 13, 27; 37:36; 39:1; Leviticus 25:44ff). Criminals could become slaves for their crimes—which we do today with prisons (see Exodus 22:3). A person could become a slave to pay off a debt (Exodus

21; Deuteronomy 15:12–18). A person could even sell themselves into slavery (Leviticus 25:39–43). There were rules about how the slaves should be treated and how a slave could be entertained, but God did not destroy the social institution of a culture to establish his way of life. Jesus lived under a government that did horrible things including slavery, but his emphasis was on the spiritual and he was not a political activist. Christianity is not a western cultural phenomenon nor an American institution. It can function in any political system including communism, a dictatorship, or a democracy.

2. THE SURROUNDING VERSES EXPLAIN THE CLAIMED ERROR.

A classic example of this situation is seen when you look at the writing that was on the sign placed on the cross over Jesus' head by Pilate. Matthew 27:37 says that the sign said "This is Jesus the king of the Jews." Mark 15:26 says the sign read "The King of the Jews." John 19:19 says the sign said "Jesus of Nazareth, the King of the Jews." Who is right? If you read the surrounding verses in John's writings you will see that verse 20 tells us that the sign was there in three languages—Aramaic, Latin, and Greek.

Atheists have made a major issue out of the fact that the order of the creation sequence in Genesis 1 and Genesis 2 are not the same. Those who endorse the documentary hypothesis have claimed that the difference in the accounts proves there were several authors to Genesis, not just Moses. If you read on in Genesis 2 you will see that the author explains why the second chapter is different than the first, and what in fact the purpose of the Genesis 2 account was. In verse 24 we read "Therefore shall a man leave his father and mother and cling to his wife and they shall become one flesh." The second chapter does not have the purpose of giving the history of the creation account. The author of the second chapter says that his purpose in writing the chapter was to show the relationship between man and woman. Chapters 1 and 2 complement each other and have a logical sequence of ideas. The author of the second chapter assumes you read the first chapter and goes on to explain the vital concept of marriage and what God intended for marriage to be.

3. THERE IS A COPYIST ERROR.

When a person says they believe the Bible is inspired, they are not talking about the words in whatever translation they are looking at. Anyone can sit down and do their own translation of the Bible, and many have done that. From the first writing of the book(s) of the Bible there could be a problem with the copyist due to the nature of how the book(s) were reproduced. Prior to the printing press the only way to get a copy of a letter or book was to copy it by hand. A scribe in a group would copy as he heard the text being read or when by himself would copy the text as he read the text. Thus a mistake could be made by not hearing or reading correctly from the "original" and this could be multiplied when one is copying from a copy.

An easy copyist error to see is in 1 Kings 4:26 where we are told that Solomon had 40,000 stalls. In a parallel passage in 2 Chronicles 9:25 the Bible says Solomon had 4,000 stalls. Both passages say he had 12,000 horsemen, so 40,000 is not reasonable. The problem is that the Hebrew word for 40 is *arbaim* and the Hebrew word for 4 is *arbah*. Since Hebrew does not use vowels a copyist since the original added some vowels or misunderstood the word being copied and created a conflict.

Another example is in Genesis 6:4 where the King James reports that there were giants in the earth. The King James translation of this verse was translated from the Vulgate (the Latin version). When the Catholic scholars translated the Hebrew word *nephilim* into Latin they chose to use the Latin word *gigantus*. The King James translators did not know what to do with that Latin word, so they brought it across untranslated and called it giant. That is not the concept.

The Hebrew word *nephilim* literally means "fallen ones." A fallen one can be an angel that rejected God or humans that rejected God. Genesis 6 is the account of humans who rejected God which culminated in the flood of Noah. It has nothing to do with giants and is another good example of why you occasionally have to go back and look at the original word in a passage to avoid what appears to be a conflict when in fact it may just be a bad translation.

4. IT IS ASSUMED THE STATEMENTS ARE IDENTICAL INSTEAD OF SEQUENTIAL.

A good example of this problem is the question of who came to Jesus' tomb and when. Mark 16:2 says that Mary came to the tomb very early when the sun had risen. John 20:1 says that Mary came to the tomb before sunrise while it was still dark. Matthew 28:1 has a completely different Mary story than either of these with two Marys coming and meeting angels.

The problem here is that these three passages are not describing the same visit. There are three visits taking place at three different times with different Marys involved. Many times there is an economy of language in the Bible and details are not given that if we are prone to do so, could lead us to assume an incorrect sequence of events took place. The Bible concentrates on its message without spending massive amounts of space making sure that every incidental event or person in the situation is explained.

5. IT IS ASSUMED THAT BECAUSE GOD TOLERATES SOMETHING, THAT HE ENDORSES IT.

A good example of this problem is polygamy. We all know that many biblical characters had more than one wife—especially in the Old Testament. God had told man in Genesis 2:24 that he was to have one wife and that the man and his wife were to become one. In spite of that Lamech takes two wives in Genesis 4:19–26. In Deuteronomy 17:17 God commands one wife, but Solomon takes hundreds of wives as God pleads with him not to do it (1 Kings 11:1–9). God is tolerant and does not force the issue, but he does tell mankind what will happen if man engages in polygamy. The multiple wives cause massive problems for man, but this is all because man refuses to do what God said.

In the New Testament Jesus tells the Jews that God tolerated these things "Because of the hardness of your hearts" (Matthew 19:1–11). When God gave instructions for leaders of the church called bishops and deacons in 1 Timothy 3:2, 12, he specified that they were to have only one wife. What God wanted man to have in marriage is described in Ephesians 5:22–32 and 1 Corinthians 7:2.

God never commanded polygamy, warned against it, and tried to teach man what a wonderful thing marriage could be with one man and one wife for life. Tragically, that concept has been lost on modern man, but God tolerates things he does not want man to have.

6. WHEN THE BIBLE REPORTS HISTORY IT ENDORSES WHAT WAS DONE.

The Bible does not white wash its heroes. David's horrible sin with Bathsheba is reported, but it certainly is not endorsed. A man named Jephthah makes a vow that he will sacrifice to God whatever comes out of his house, if God will give him a victory (Judges 11:30–40). God did not command that and in fact, God has always discouraged careless vows on the part of his people. In this case Jephthah's daughter was the first thing that came out to him after the victory. This was not a case of God commanding human sacrifice as atheists have claimed. Exactly what was done with the girl can be argued, but the message is a message about vows, not a command of God that man should engage in human sacrifice. The incident is reported but certainly was not condoned or commanded by God.

Another example is Judges 20:5–7 where a woman is raped to death and she is cut up into pieces and her body parts sent throughout Israel to rally a response to what had been done. This awful story is a news report, not a religious act done at the command of God. We all know that whatever is on the evening news is not something the station or the news reporter necessarily endorses, and that is true of the Bible as well.

Chapter 9

EVOLUTION

Any discussion of the accuracy of the Bible, and whether the Bible is the word of God or not, will eventually bring up the subject of evolution. Our most basic position in this book is that science and faith are not enemies, they are friends. If there is a conflict between faith and science we either had some bad theology, some bad science, or both. The lesson of history is that we have had a lot of both. When you stop and think about it, a real conflict is impossible if in fact God was the Creator and if in fact God gave us the Bible. If God did the creating, and then God told us what he did, how can they possibly conflict? If there appears to be a conflict it is bad theology or bad science or both.

The first problem to occur in this situation is carelessness in defining terms. What do we mean by "evolution?" Religious people have sometimes responded to this question by saying "amoeba to man" or "monkey to man." There have been those in the scientific community who have radiated the idea that evolution and naturalism are the same thing. The fact is that the word "evolution" according to *Merriam-Webster's Dictionary* is to "unroll out" or the "process of unrolling." No rational person questions whether this occurs or not. In agriculture we have all seen new breeds of cattle, sheep, dogs and hybridization in a variety of plants has given us everything from the Nancy Reagan rose to RoundUp tolerant corn.

There are hundreds of different pedigrees of dogs and of roses. The production of all of these "new" forms is done by evolution.

In recent years it has become fashionable to talk about microevolution and macroevolution. The examples above would all be considered to be microevolutionary changes. To suggest that a cow evolved from a certain reptile would be a macroevolutionary change. The definition of macroevolution is usually stated to be "any evolutionary change at or above the level of species." The problem with that definition is that the word "species" is very difficult to define and apply. In most high school textbooks the definition would read something like this: "A species is a group of plants or animals that can interbreed and produce fertile offspring." A horse and a donkey can reproduce and produce offspring, but the offspring will be sterile and is called a mule. A canary and some other kind of finch can mate and produce infertile offspring. By this definition horses and donkeys or canaries and all other finches are different species. There have been reports of mules not being sterile, and sometimes scientists are surprised at animals that mate successfully and produce fertile offspring that were previously thought to be different species. Several different species of monkeys are examples and there have been crosses between various goats and sheep producing an animal which has been called a geep. Sometimes physical limitations make mating impossible (like a Saint Bernard and a Chihuahua) and yet in a test tube, conception is possible. Even with man the question has been raised, because the genetic similarity between chimpanzees and man is well over 95% and yet variation among various races of man can be well over 5%.

Figure 9.1: Lisa the geep ... a cross between a goat and a sheep (a sheep-goat hybrid)
http://www.dailymail.co.uk/news/article-513047/How-night-passion-sheep-goat-led-Lisa-GEEP.html

The point is that the question of where microevolution ends and macroevolution begins is very difficult to agree on. The bigger question is whether the processes we are talking about preclude God's role in the creation of all living things, or whether their existence is a reflection of the wisdom and design built into the creation. Dr. Francis Collins, the director of the Human Genome Project that has mapped the entire DNA sequence of humans is a believer in God. He has written a book titled *The Language of God* in which he maintains that all of this is a tool of God to achieve God's purposes. The main problem with such an approach is that what science believes about the process now is radically different than it was even five years ago, and if you adjust your theological beliefs on the current model of science your theology is constantly changing as science shifts its understandings.

When someone says "Evolution is a fact" the main issue is what do you mean by evolution, and do you mean evolution or do you mean naturalism. Naturalism is not a fact, it is a philosophical belief, that everything can ultimately be explained by science, which is not consistent with the evidence. What is more important in this discussion is what the Bible actually does say, and how what it says jibes with the facts that are available to us.

Biblical "Kinds"

A part of the solution to the above problems is to evaluate all the models of evolution by comparing them to the Genesis account of creation. In so doing, we find that much of the confusion caused by atheistic evolution disappears. Genesis states that God created life forms in the seas, air, and land to reproduce "after their kind." The word "kind" in Hebrew (*min*) is a broad term defined later in the New Testament (1 Corinthians 15:39) to mean four separate forms of "flesh"—the flesh of fish, birds, beasts, and humans.

These biblical "kinds" correspond more closely with our modern taxonomic category of class rather than species, as shown in figure 9.2. This chart uses the robin as an example of the classification system in use today. The robin is one of 9,700 known species of birds that are all of the same class, Aves.

In view of this definition, the questions arise—did God separately create everyone of the 9,700-plus species of birds, or did he design birds with the ability to adapt to many different environmental settings.

Level	Bird (Robin)	Fish	Beast	Human
Kingdom	Animalia	Animalia	Animalia	Animalia
Phylum	Chordata	Chordata	Chordata	Chordata
Class	**Aves**	**Pisces**	**Mammalia**	**Mammalia**
Order	Passeriformes			Primates
Family	Turdidae			Hominidae
Genus	*Turdus*			*Homo*
Species	*migratorious*			*sapiens*

Figure 9.2: Assumed biblical taxonomy of life

Before going further with this discussion of species and kinds, it is important to identify a concept that is vital to understanding the biblical account correctly.

Ancient creation myths in general describe monster gods and goddesses, frost-giants, and feathered serpents creating the earth and humans from dismembered goddesses, trees, and tears. The Genesis account contrasts sharply with these stories, even though the Bible does not claim to be a book of science.

In 2 Timothy 3:16–17, the Bible does make the claim, "All Scripture is God-breathed and is useful for teaching, rebuking, correcting and training in righteousness, so that the man of God may be thoroughly equipped for every good work."

The Bible teaches about how God's relationship with us and how our relationship with him will motivate us to reflect his love in doing good works for others. It tells us why we are here on the earth and where we are going. That is the reason some commentators have said that the Bible tells us about the Who and Why of creation, and science supplies the What, How, and When.

The book of Genesis is the first in a five-book section of the Bible known as the Pentateuch. The author is presumed to be Moses, who wrote and/or compiled the Genesis information around 1300–1500 B.C. in the vicinity of the land of Egypt. The introduction describes one supreme God who created the heavens and the earth without giving prominence to the gods of Egypt, particularly the sun. This was a strong theological statement against Egyptian polytheism and sun worship. God's creation framework of a seven-

An Unpolluted Creation Account

This first chapter [of Genesis] is so ancient that it does not contain mythical or legendary matter; these elements are entirely absent. It bears the markings of having been written before myth and legend had time to grow, and not as is often stated, at a later date when it had to be stripped of the mythical and legendary elements inherent in every other account of Creation extant. This account is so original that it does not bear a trace of any system of philosophy. Yet it is so profound that it is capable of correcting philosophical systems. It is so ancient that it contains nothing that is merely nationalistic; neither Babylonian, Egyptian, nor Jewish modes of thought find a place in it, for it was written before clans, nations, or philosophies originated. Surely, we must regard it as the original, of which the other extant accounts are merely corrupted copies. Others incorporate their national philosophies in crude polytheistic and mythological form. This is pure. Genesis 1 is as primitive as the first human. It is the threshold of written history (Wiseman 1985, 90).

day week with its symbolic seventh day of rest also set the example for the sabbath law soon to be given to the nation of Israel at Mount Sinai.

ORIGINAL AUDIENCE
Scientific World-View

Recognizing this religious purpose in the Genesis account of creation makes us realize that the book should not be viewed as a scientific treatise written to challenge the technological minds of our day. It was originally penned to be understood by both shepherds and scholars whose world-view was shaped by the primitive cultures in which they lived.

Not appreciating this causes some modern critics of the Bible to complain because, in their opinion, Genesis is not nearly complicated enough to be from God. They believe it should read something like, "In the beginning God synthesized DNA in a kaolinite matrix, enzymatically catalyzed by … ."

If those were the words used to reveal God's creative acts to Moses, think how difficult it would have been for Moses to understand the relevance of what God said. Such specialized language would have confused and puzzled people for ages until humans advanced enough in scientific knowledge to comprehend its significance. Fortunately, God's mission was not to confuse and misdirect Moses or any readers of the text who followed him.

As it was, no ancient reader had ever seen the earth from outer space or had leafed through a world atlas or consulted a globe. In fact, in the entire Bible, there is no original-language word for planet earth. Because of limited traveling experiences, most people's idea of the ends of the earth often consisted of what they could see from the top of the highest local hill. The heavens were equally limited by their observations, with the sun and moon appearing to be bright discs traveling across a tentlike sky.

Against this background, the first chapters of Genesis become both simple and profound. The basic message is that one supreme God created everything, including the first man and woman. They were set apart from all other living things because they were created in the very image of their maker. God omitted many of the details regarding when, where, and why he chose to create the first couple in this way. He gave what appears to be just enough information to satisfy our basic curiosity about where we came from and where we are going.

Language Differences

We also need to understand that the Bible was not written in English for an American audience. It was written in Hebrew for all audiences, and that means translation is necessary. Any time a translation is made, certain problems arise. Let me demonstrate this to you with Spanish.

I know nothing about Spanish, so when I hear, "Juan tiene frio," I have to look up what it means. When I find that the words literally mean, "John has cold," I wonder if it means that John has a cold (that he is ill) or if it means that John is cold (that he is shivering).

My wife, who took Spanish in high school, tells me that it means, "John is cold." I ask her, "How do you know that?" and she replies, "I took Spanish in school, and they explained that the culture would understand it that way."

Another example that is more complicated would be, "Juan me cae bien gordo." Literally translated, this phrase reads, "John me falls well fat." This is not a comment about my weight, it simply means, "I don't like John very much." From these examples, it should be apparent that literal translations can easily give mistaken concepts if the culture from which the translation is made is not considered.

Bara

Contextual translation such as this becomes very relevant to a literal understanding of Genesis 1. In the original Hebrew language, there are two concepts about how God brings things into existence. One way God operates is by a miraculous process that only God can do. The Hebrew word *bara* was used to indicate this process.

Bara is never used in reference to something humans can do. It is a term reserved exclusively to describe God's actions in the creation. The Jewish Publication Society says, "The Hebrew *bara* is used in the Bible exclusively of divine creativity. It signifies that the product is absolutely novel and unexampled, depends solely upon God for its coming into existence and is beyond the human capacity to reproduce" (Sarna, 1989).

The Jewish scholar Leiden says, "We have in our holy language no other term for 'the bringing forth of something from nothing' but *bara*" (1960). Appendix 7 (page 201) contains the King James translation of Genesis 1 with the words in Hebrew written above the words in English. You will notice that *bara* is used in Genesis 1:1 and again in Genesis 1:21 and 1:27.

Asah and Yatsar

In addition to bara, there is another way God can bring things into existence. This is a process that does not always involve a miracle, but rather is a shaping or molding of something already created. The Hebrew words used to describe this process are *asah* and *yatsar*. These words are not used just in reference to accomplishments that only God can do; they are also used in reference to things that humans can do.

We see examples of *asah* in phrases like "make me laugh," "make a feast," and "make war." These are generally not miracles, but ordinary actions that humans can take by personal choice. In the biblical record, God also *asah*s much of what is described in Genesis 1:2–19.

Yatsar is used in Genesis 2:7, 8, and 19 and means to mold or squeeze into shape as a potter would work with clay. Many people have not taken the Bible literally in regard to the meaning of these three Hebrew words as they are used in the creation account. Rather, the assertion is made that *bara* and *asah* both mean to create miraculously in a way that only God can do.

One of the texts often used to argue against a literal interpretation is the scripture that discusses the formation of man. In Genesis 1:27, we are told that God created (*bara*) man in his own image; and yet in Genesis 2:7, the Bible says God formed (*yatsar*) man from the dust of the ground. Are these two verses referring to the same thing?

The answer is emphatically no! Genesis 1:27 is describing that which is in God's image — the spiritual makeup of humans. Genesis 2:7 is referring to man's body — that which is made of the dust of the earth and will eventually return to the dust. The two words are relating to completely different subjects.

A further challenge might come from Genesis 1:26 where God says, "Let us make *(asah)* man in our image … ." In this context, the statement is made within the Godhead, not in the physical world. The "us" in the passage is the Father, Son, and Holy Spirit and is spoken from their point of view. The process is not miraculous to them because it is something they ordinarily do in their heavenly realm.

In other words, it is said that God created the universe out of nothing. However, we now know that matter and energy are equivalent. Therefore, God did not create out of nothing. From his perspective, he "made" *(asah)* the human spirit out of himself, so to speak, since he is the source of all energy (Isaiah 40:26; Hebrews 12:9). From our perspective, though, God literally created (*bara*) the human spirit because it was not formed from anything material,

How Much Energy Exists in Our Universe

The amount of energy in our universe is incalculable, since the amount of pure energy used in the creation of only one gram of matter (1/450th of a pound) is equal to 2.5 times the amount of energy generated by Niagara Falls in one day. This would be 10 million kilowatts of energy (Willmington).

but came directly from his dimension or dwelling place, which is outside our tangible universe (John 14:2).

To be sure that we do not misunderstand this vital point regarding the two aspects of creation, the Bible ends the creation story by saying that God "rested from all his work which God created (*bara*) and made (*asah*)" (Genesis 2:3). According to God, both processes were used. First, everything was created somewhere within the big-bang event, and then, over time, the material universe was formed or made out of that which was originally created.

Genesis 2:3 speaks of God both creating (Hebrew, *bara*, meaning to make miraculously out of nothing) and making (Hebrew, *asah*, meaning to mold or shape something already created).

Since both words are used to describe God's creative acts, it appears that he may have equipped animal DNA with the ability to microevolve within the general bounds of an animal's class, which the Bible refers to as kind. In other words, the Bible and the fossil record would be in precise agreement if God programmed the DNA molecule to produce a wide variety of life forms within each animal class. When the need for change became too great, God would produce a new and different kind of animal by creatively "tinkering" with its genetic "tool kit." This exciting, relatively new concept is known as "basic type biology" (Hartwig-Scherer 1998, 215).

If this hypothesis is correct, then, to the consternation of the evolutionary community, we should find evidence for both gradual and rapid changes taking place within the fossil record. This very conclusion is summarized well in the book *Understanding Human Evolution*, which says:

Although there is considerable disagreement among pale-ontologists, evidence for both gradual evolutionary change and for the punctuated equilibrium* model can be gleaned from the fossil record. There is very heated debate on this point. It should not surprise us, however, that evidence seems to exist for both evolutionary models (Poirier and McKee 1999, 34).

Again, we should ask ourselves, Is it just another coincidence that the Bible specifically says that God both "created" and "made" all the living things around us?

*Punctuated equilibrium: evolution that is characterized by long periods of stability in the characteristics of an organism and short periods of rapid change during which new forms appear especially from small subpopulations of the ancestral form in restricted parts of its geographic range. Source: http://www.merriam-webster.com/dictionary/punctuated equilibrium (accessed: November 01, 2011)

10

THE AGE OF THE EARTH

There is probably no religious belief that has caused more problems in modern times than dispensationalism. Ronald L. Numbers in his book *The Creationists* has shown that a vast percentage of fundamental creationists have based their beliefs on dispensationalism. Christian Zionism, in which churches are actively involved in promoting the Nation of Israel, is rooted in this belief system. Over half of Protestant denominations hold to dispensationalism in one form or another, and virtually all "televangelists" promote it including John Hagee, Jerry Falwell, Jim Bakker, Paul Crouch, Pat Robertson, Jimmy Swaggart, and Billy Graham. Other well known dispensationalists include Tim LaHaye, Hal Lindsey, Charles Ryrie, John Walvoord, and Eric Sauer. Several well-known Christian organizations also promote it including Moody Bible Institute and Dallas Theological Seminary.

John Nelson Darby, Cyrus Scofield, and D. L. Moody were the architects of dispensationalism early in the twentieth century. The basic claim was that in 2 Timothy 2:15 when Paul told Timothy to "rightly divide the word of truth" that he was to divide it into seven discrete dispensations. Various dispensationalists had different views of how the seven dispensations were to be identified including Scofield's version which is built into the famous *Scofield Study Bible*. While different early dispensational preachers had different understandings and views, their basic belief system was constant. They all viewed the seven dispensations to be leading to the reestablishment of Israel as a world power with Jerusalem as the capital of the world and Jesus the supreme King of the world.

Most dispensational systems broke their seven dispensations into something like this:

Innocence	Genesis 1:3 – 3:6
Conscience	Genesis 3:7 – 8:14
Civil Government	Genesis 8:15 – 11:9
Patriarchal Rule	Genesis 11:10 – Exodus 18:27
Mosaic Law	Exodus 19:1 – John 14:30
Grace	Acts 1:1 – Revelation 19:21
Millennium	Revelation 20:1 – 15

In dispensational tradition there is a permanent distinction made between Israel, the Gentiles, and the Church. Lewis Chafer, the founder of Dallas Theological Seminary put it this way: "The dispensationalist believes that throughout the ages God is pursuing two distinct purposes: one related to the earth with earthly people and earthly objectives involved, which is Judaism; while the other is related to heavenly people and heavenly objectives involved, which is Christianity. Israel is an eternal nation, heir to an eternal land, and with an eternal kingdom, on which David rules from an eternal throne." Dispensationalists go on to say that the promises made to Abraham and through him to the Jews are eternal, unconditional, and await future realization so that the land promised to Abraham and his descendants from the Nile to the Euphrates will be literally instituted and that Jesus Christ will return to a Jewish kingdom centered on a rebuilt temple in Jerusalem.

Many dispensationalists believe that when the Jewish nation was reestablished in Palestine in 1948 that it was an indication that this was the generation when all of this was to take place. Very shortly then, in this belief, there will be a rapture in which Christ appears in the heavens and resurrects all dead Christians and together with all living believers takes them into heaven for seven years. During this seven years God is said to anoint 144,000 Jews to be missionaries for Christ. The Roman empire is revived as the European Common Market. The "Antichrist" solves the world's problems and becomes the world dictator in Rome. A second "Antichrist" arises to govern Israel in collaboration with the Roman ruler. Israel rebuilds the temple and reestablishes Jewish worship including animal sacrifices. Arab countries, Russia, and Red China get involved and Christ returns with resurrected Christians to end the war and rules on David's throne for 1,000 years. Later there is a final judgment for all of the wicked of all ages.

There are many variations of this scenario, and there are many detailed studies of the claims which show biblically why it is an incorrect theological view. Many dispensationalists take the reference to 1,000 in passages like Revelation 20:2–3 to mean that the dispensations were all roughly that long. That makes the earth about 6,000 years old, and puts certain events in man's history in the very recent past. Even such cities as Bejing, China, with city records going back far longer than 6,000 years have to be changed to fit this theology. Evidence continues to pile up from all areas of man's studies in geology, astronomy, archeology, history, and genetics that this simply is not the case.

Dispensationalism is a man-made theology that is in conflict with the evidence, the Bible, and common sense. We must not borrow from its teachings in science, history, or politics because when we do we not only mislead ourselves, but we make God's Word look foolish.

Some of the previous paragraphs are from "Orchestrating the End" by Stephen Sizer, *SCP Journal*, Volume 31:4 & 32:1, 2008, page 52.

THE NATURE OF SCIENTIFIC DATING TECHNIQUES

We are not just interested in what the stories are that the fossils have to tell us, but we are also interested in when those stories took place. When we find a plant-eating dinosaur with a *Tyrannosaurus rex* tooth imbedded in its hip bone, we would like to date the bite. There are several problems in embarking on this subject. One of them is the question of uniformitarianism (see page 124). How long did it take to produce the Grand Canyon? I have a commercial film-strip that I was given by the school system to show in my classroom that makes the calculation this way: It assumes that the Canyon was produced by the Colorado River eroding down through an uplifted plateau. At the present time, the Colorado River is eroding about one half a foot every 1,000 years. That means it takes 2,000 years to erode each foot of rock. If there is 6,000 feet of rock missing and it takes 2,000 years for each foot, then obviously the time to erode the Canyon is 6,000 feet times 2,000 thousand years per foot or 12,000,000 years.

What assumptions are made in this calculation? The reader might wish to stop and write down the ones they see. First of all, we have to assume that the Colorado River did in fact cause the canyon. It is undoubtedly one agent, but not the only agent. The whole canyon is a monocline (a fold) which affects the erosion rate. There are literally hundreds of faults in the canyon which changes the ease of erosion. The rock types in the Canyon vary with some being softer than others and thus are easier to erode. The volume of water in the Colorado River is certainly not constant and, before the dams were built on it, certainly had greater cutting ability. There have been lava flows which dammed up the river and made a lake which would profoundly alter the rocks in the area. The list of assumptions that have to be made goes on and on — all of which would alter the calculated age of the canyon. All dating methods have similar assumptions and are based on uniformitarianism. There have been creationists who have attempted to compare erosion rates on Mount Saint Helens to the Grand Canyon, but Mount Saint Helens is a volcano. Volcanic rocks are much easier to erode than sedimentary rocks, so assumptions are being made in the creationist camp that are as bad as those incorporated by those attaching long ages to the production of the Canyon.

There are some dating methods which are better than others and some that have fewer assumptions than others. In polar areas, there is an interesting phenomena associated with snowfall. In the winter it snows, and in the summer it does not snow. It never gets very warm in many areas during the summer, however, and the accumulation of snow from the previous winter does not melt. It snows again the next winter so the snow piles up on the last snow and the next summer it does not melt again. The total pile of snow gets higher and higher, and the snow gets fused into ice. During the summer months when the snow does not melt, it does get covered with summer debris—insects, dust, pollen, and a variety of plant material. This means that there are lines in the snow and ice that can be looked at with a microscope and the lines can be counted like the growth rings on a tree. This is a method that is much different than some of the others. There are over 500 methods of dating used by scientists, historians, archaeologists, and chemists. When more than one of these methods are used, they usually give similar results, and none of them give an age to man or to life as small as 10,000 years.

BIBLICAL TIME

How old does the Bible say that man, life in general, and the earth are? The first point that needs to be made is that God can do whatever God likes! God has the power to create the cosmos as it is, with you sitting there reading this, the paper in your hands, the memories in your head, and all that surrounds you good and bad—all of that could have been created two seconds ago or even less. God does not need time at all! If we understand God as the Bible defines and describes him, then time is a creation of God and does not control God. The issue is not what God *could* do but what he *did* do. The evidence is that you have been sitting there more than three seconds, and the evidence is that the Creation happened more than 10,000 years ago.

Any attempt to date the earth biblically has to make assumptions just as the scientific methods have to make assumptions. In 1650, Archbishop James Ussher of the Episcopalian Church stated beautifully the most fundamental assumptions:

1. There are no undated verses in the biblical account.
2. There are no missing people in biblical genealogies.
3. The purpose of the genealogies was chronological, so they are all written in chronological order.
4. No historical period is missing from the Bible.

Any dating method that attempts to use the Bible as a basis will have to use these assumptions, and yet all of these assumptions are wrong! Let us take a look at them:

Assumption 1. There are many undated verses and events in the Bible. How long were Adam and Eve in the Garden of Eden? I have a male chauvinistic friend who says, "Knowing my wife, it couldn't possibly have been more than 10 minutes"; but that is an assumption with great consequences. I would suggest that Adam's age was measured from the time he began to die—not from his creation, so the time in the Garden cannot even be related to his age.

Another example of an undated verse or event in the Bible is Genesis 1:1–3. Denominational tradition has taught us that the first three verses of Genesis are a summary of the rest of the chapter. For years, people have read Genesis 1:1 like this: "In the beginning God created the heaven and earth and, in the next 31 verses, I am going to tell you everything God did." That is simply not what it says. These verses are a historical narrative written in a historical style. Notice the wording:

When?
"In the beginning"
Something happened. What was it?
"God created the heaven and the earth"
What happened next?
"The earth was (or became, as some versions say) without
    form and void; and darkness was upon the face of the
    deep."
What happened next?
"the Spirit of God moved upon the face of the waters."

These are historical events written in a historical sequence. They are not summary verses of what is to follow. Something is happening in each of the statements that are made, and the things that are happening are undated and untimed.

Assumptions 2 and 3. It is clear that biblical genealogies were not written for chronological purposes nor are they supposed to be interpreted as being complete. In the book of Ezra, for example, there are four people listed in the genealogy between Azariah and

Amariah. In 1 Chronicles 6:3–14, the same genealogical sequence is given, but this time there are 12 people listed in the same sequence. The genealogy of 1 Chronicles 3:11–12 does not agree with Matthew 1:1–17 which has Uzziah's father, grandfather, and great-grandfather omitted. In fact, Matthew gives 42 steps in the same genealogy for which Luke gives 56 steps. Some have pointed out that Luke records Mary's side of the family instead of Joseph's, (see page 96 for more on this topic) but that does not explain 13 missing generations.

The point is that these writings were not written by people living in the twenty-first century. In ancient times, people did not give complete listings of their family tree when giving their ancestry. What they usually listed were the famous people in their lineage. In Matthew 1:1, for example, the genealogy of Jesus is given as follows: "Jesus Christ, the son of David, the son of Abraham." It is obvious that Jesus was not Abraham's grandson, but that is in fact what the passage says. It is not an error; it is simply that genealogies were never written in the Bible with the idea that it would be used to calculate time or to establish chronology. Lineage is the only message of the biblical genealogies.

Assumption 4. It is totally obvious that the Bible does not include a number of historical events. The time between Malachi and Matthew is an obvious example, but there are many others that can be given. There are cases in the Bible where genealogies are reversed; for example, Noah's sons are listed in reverse order.

The point of this discussion is that, like the scientific methods of dating, biblical methods of dating involve a large number of assumptions which make any attempt to give a biblical age to the creation or to Adam doomed to failure. There is no reason to use the Bible in this way unless your denominational tradition forces you to. If your denominational creed teaches that the history of the earth involves seven time periods of about 1,000 years each, the last of which is said to be the physical reign of Christ upon the earth, then you have to find a way to limit the age of the earth to a relatively small number. This is a case of a human belief system forcing something on the Bible which the Bible does not say. It seems to this author that it is more logical and consistent to simply admit that this is not a biblical issue, and whether the earth is 6 seconds old, 6 days old, 6 millennia old, or 6 trillion years old does not matter.

What we have suggested in this discussion is not new. Many years ago, conservative biblical students who took the Bible literally instead of accepting the teachings of human beings said the same thing we have tried to articulate. David Lipscomb said in 1921, "I have no way of knowing how long the world was created before man was created. The Bible does not tell. It only says, 'In the beginning' and that afterwards He created the plants and animals, and last of all man. But it gives no intimation how long the earth was created before these other things were" (*Questions Answered by Lipscomb and Sewell*, Gospel Advocate Co., Nashville, TN, 1974, page 747. Originally published by McQuiddy Printing Co. in 1921). Foy E. Wallace said, "There is no statement in the Bible which indicates the age of the earth … . If the scientist or pseudoscientists want to ascribe to the earth an age of a million, a billion, or three hundred billion years, I will not pause to argue … . 'In the beginning God.' That is all the Bible affirms on the question" (*God's Prophetic Word* by Foy E. Wallace, The Roy E. Cogdill Publishing Co., Lufkin, TX, 1946, page 6).

ARGUMENTS FOR FLOOD GEOLOGY

Proponents of a young earth claim that the global flood described in Genesis 7 and 8 was responsible for the fossil record as we have it today. This flood, accompanied by earthquakes, volcanic eruptions, and powerful surge waves, is believed to have caused extensive erosion of soil and rock beds, burying plants and animals in the shifting mud and redepositing the soils elsewhere in stratified layers (Whitcomb and Morris 1961/1998, 123). The order of fossils in the rocks from simple to complex and from sea creatures to land animals is claimed to be the natural result of their flight to escape the flood.

In other words, the rising waters would have sorted out the life forms according to size and mobility. The smaller, less mobile creatures would occupy the lower layers of earth's rocks because they would have been the first to be buried. The larger, more mobile creatures would have run to higher ground only to be buried later. Whitcomb and Morris go on to state that the remaining humans and animals swept away at the very last "would not be buried but simply drowned and then carried about by the waters on or near the surface until finally decomposed by the elements" (1961/1998, 266).

According to this scenario, the flood would be totally responsible for the entire geologic column deposited since the Cambrian period estimated by scientists to have started some 550 million years ago. Likewise, the Grand Canyon would not have been caused by slow erosion cutting through solid rock over millions of years as the land gradually uplifted. Rather, it would have been formed by the rapid drainage of a series of lakes located to the east.

About two hundred years after the flood had laid down most of the deposits evident to an observer in the Grand Canyon today, natural earth and stone dams retaining these inland lakes would have broken, releasing a huge volume of water, mud, and boulders that would have quickly pulverized the newly formed rock into dust as it cut a canyon through the soft material on its westward course. A recent example of such rapid erosion took place at Mount Saint Helens when a river of water and mud raced through 600 feet of recently placed volcanic ash and formed a deep canyon in that location. Therefore, it is reasoned that the same type of event could have rapidly formed the Grand Canyon (Brown et al. 1996).

These brief and very simplified explanations for the formation of the geologic record and the Grand Canyon are two examples of how proponents of creation science believe cataclysmic events by the hand of God shaped the world as we see it in less than 10,000 years.

ARGUMENTS AGAINST FLOOD GEOLOGY

Although young earth supporters Paul Nelson and John Mark Reynolds are excited about the potential for creation science research, they honestly admit that as a science "young earth creationism is generally underdeveloped" and that a recent paper presented on flood geology provides "a huge amount of room for future research" (1999, 98).

The first problem with flood geology is the nature of the rocks that are in places like the Grand Canyon. There are three kinds of rocks known to science—sedimentary rocks, metamorphic rocks, and igneous rocks. Igneous rocks are formed in molten circumstances, and that is not what the flood would have been about. Metamorphic rocks are changed rocks and again are not the predominant rocks in places like the Grand Canyon. The kind of rocks laid down in what flood geology proponents describe are sedimentary rocks. There are two kinds of sedimentary rocks—clastic rocks and chemical precipitates. Clastic rocks are what flood deposits would be. Mud, sand, and gravel are deposited by running water and/or wind and turned into rock. Mud turned into rock becomes shale. Sand turned into rock becomes sandstone. Gravel turned into rock becomes conglomerate or breccia depending on how rounded the cobbles are in the gravel. This is what a flood produces. When someone is flooded out they come home to a house full of mud, sand, gravel, and massive debris. They are not chiseling limestone off of the piano.

Limestone is a chemically precipitated rock. This kind of rock forms slowly in quiet conditions over protracted periods of time. A jar of jelly forgotten on a cellar shelf will have sugar crystals growing in the jelly. Maple syrup that is not shaken or stirred will have the same thing happen. If someone stirs or shakes the syrup the big crystals will not form. A flood would never produce a chemically precipitated rock—and yet most of the rocks in the Grand Canyon, Niagara Falls, etc., are chemically precipitated rocks—limestones, dolomites, gypsum, etc.

One unique characteristic about limestone is that it gets harder with time. Indiana oolitic limestone is a famous building stone quarried not far from where I grew up, and it is uniquely qualified to be a building stone because of this characteristic. Mount Saint Helens is a volcano, and the erosion that takes place there is an erosion of volcanic ash. This ash is soft, easily carried by running water, and dissolves in running water. How many buildings have you seen made of volcanic ash? Any comparison between Mount Saint Helens and the Grand Canyon is totally invalid.

The average junior high student who has had a course in earth science knows what I have just described to you. If the preacher gets up on Sunday morning and states that the Grand Canyon was produced by the flood of Noah, and the students know what I have just explained to you, what happens? If the preacher is wrong in this matter, why should I trust what he says in any matter? There are many other reasons why the canyon cannot have been produced by the flood of Noah. There are many other proofs that the flood did not cause the Grand Canyon and other structures like it, so we have just explored the petrology problems — the rock issues.

THE NATURE OF FOSSILS

I was a high school earth science teacher. I took my advanced degree work in a program sponsored by the National Science Foundation and, since it was government sponsored and involved locations all over the United States, I was able to see first-hand the geology of North America. I have been blessed by being able to travel throughout North America and parts of Europe and Australia and have been able to see major points of geologic interest in those areas. I also have been able to collect large numbers of fossils from all kinds of living things and all sorts of geologic formations. Any standard geology textbook, museum, or encyclopedia will show you pictures of fossils. The fossils have many stories to tell us about the past. A fossil can be defined as any evidence of life that has lived on the earth in the past. This means it can be a bone, a piece of skin, a footprint, the dung of an animal, a nest, an egg, or the imprint of one of these.

The lessons seen in the fossils are many and varied. We see animals that have lived in the past that are very different than animals living today, and we see that the conditions under which they lived were also very different. I have seen the fossils of tropical animals in Alaska. I have seen coal deposits with a dinosaur buried in the coal deep under the ground in several places. I have seen the eggs of dinosaurs with the fossilized babies still inside at various stages of embryonic development. Dinosaurs lived, and their fossilized remains tell us a great deal about them. Michigan's state rock is the Petosky stone, a tropical coral that will not grow in water colder than 68°F. The tennis courts in Petosky, Michigan, have massive amounts of this material around them and few of us would believe that Petosky, Michigan, is a tropical paradise today! I have seen drill cores from the north slopes in Alaska where there have been redwood deposits found. Today, the intense cold prevents any plant like that from growing there.

One of the major lessons that fossils have to tell us is the nature of the history of the earth. Evolution and much of geology have assumed that the nature of the history of the earth has been a constant history. The snappy way of saying this is "the present is the key to the past." The idea is that, when we look at a rock or a fossil, we assume that the processes that produced what we are looking at have been processes that are still operational today. The processes may not have been functioning at the same *rate* that they are today, but the processes are the same. That means that all the earth has been shaped and molded by volcanoes, glaciers, earthquakes, landslides, flash floods, water erosion, weathering, etc. This assumption has been given the name uniformitarianism.

The alternative to this view would be that processes we do not see operational today have worked in the past and have been major players in shaping the earth. The biblical flood of Noah would certainly not be a uniformitarian event. The Bible actually tells us that God has created with consistency and uniformity (Numbers 23:19–20; Deuteronomy 33:15; Psalm 23:11; Psalm 104:5; Psalm 119:89–91; Matthew 3:6; James 1:17). The Bible also tells us that, on rare occasions, God has punctuated history with catastrophic events that have an effect on large sections of this planet or even on the entire earth. The flood of Noah is an example, as are the plagues in Egypt, the events when Jesus died, and certainly what will happen when he comes again.

What does the fossil record tell us about this question? There are many illustrations that can be given on this question, but the best, in this writer's opinion, is the extinction of the dinosaurs. The dinosaurs were wiped out, along with numerous other plants and animals, by an event that is not taking place today. When studies were made of the deposits in which the last remains of the dinosaurs are found, it was discovered that there were large amounts of the elements iridium, osmium, and rhenium in the deposits. These elements are found on the earth in trace amounts, but they are found in the deposits of the rocks that contain evidence of the dinosaurs' destruction in concentrations 500 times higher than normal earth rocks. These elements are found in asteroids—large chunks of rocks from outer space. Most scientists now agree that, at the end of the time when the dinosaurs lived on the earth, a large asteroid hit the earth — perhaps off the Yucatan Peninsula. There are a number of facts that support this event, and the event would explain the mass extinction of the dinosaurs and other things that disappeared from the earth.

Here is a case where the Bible was thought to have been in error about the nature of events that have occurred in the past. As the evidence has become stronger, the integrity of the biblical record has been proven. Most fossils show us a past with conditions like what we see happening today, but God has interrupted his normally hospitable conditions with an occasional catastrophe which does have a significant effect upon life. The fossil record also shows that animals very different than animals living today have existed in the past — animals that we call dinosaurs. I have met people who wanted to deny that dinosaurs ever lived on this planet, but I have seen dried out specimens in the ground with skin on their bodies. I have looked at the dung of dinosaurs and I have seen how easy it is to tell what they ate — some of the dung being full of plant material, and some of it being full of the remains of the bodies of other animals. Most of the dinosaurs were very small animals being no larger than a collie, but I have seen the remains of huge animals dwarfing most land animals of today. It is interesting to note that the largest animal ever to have lived on this planet still lives on the earth today — the blue whale. The aorta of this giant animal is so large that you could swim through it. For land animals as large as a brontosaurus to have lived on the earth, the land must have been very different than it is today. Land plants that we know today would have a hard time reproducing and growing fast enough to satisfy these animals' food needs. The plants that the dinosaurs ate were gymnosperms — fast-growing plants like ferns and conifers. Temperatures must have been high to minimize metabolic problems in the animals.

In spite of these obvious problems, there have been those who have tried to maintain that humans and dinosaurs lived at the same time. The first time I heard of any claims like this was in reference to a park in Glen Rose, Texas. A man named Jake McFall who lived near the state park just outside of Glen Rose had been involved in a film titled *Footprints in Stone* in which human and dinosaur tracks were claimed to have been found in the same rock. For a nominal fee, Jake took me to the tracks and to a number of other tracks on his farm. The tracks were sandal shaped tracks some 16 inches long, with a few of them having erosion grooves in the front that looked a little like toes. The tracks were obviously not human tracks to me, but I went on to town and the Somervell County Museum where other materials were displayed. A local man who spent a great deal of time in the museum assured me the human tracks were not real.

During the next several years, I made three more trips to Glen Rose looking at other claimed tracks and even had contact with Carl Baugh who has attempted to keep this story alive. Gene Kuban, a science teacher in Waxahatche, Texas, released a study of the tracks in 1986 in which he demonstrated that, if one cut the rocks parallel to the surface of ground, one could see that the tracks were clearly dinosaur tracks with a three-toed imprint at the bottom. The soft mud had fallen into the track leaving a sandal shaped impression that looked like a human footprint, but clearly was not. Everyone associated with the situation seemed to be in agreement. John Morris of the Institute for Creation Research was quoted in *Time* (June 30, 1986, page 75) as agreeing that there were no human tracks at Glen Rose and the film *Footprints in Stone* was withdrawn from circulation. There are still people today who are trying to maintain that humans and dinosaurs lived together, and films like *Jurassic Park* have not changed that view any. I believe that the major problem is that the only way certain religious views can be seriously entertained is to refuse to admit that the earth is much more than 6,000 years old, and that view requires dinosaurs and humans to be contemporaries.

THE HISTORY OF CREATION ACCORDING TO THE BIBLE AND THE FOSSILS

It may be helpful to the reader to use the biblical text with the Hebrew words that are listed in Appendix 7 (page 203) to follow this discussion. The first verse of Genesis is a creation (*bara*) verse, not a making (*asah*) verse. The things created, according to verse 1, are the heaven (*shamayim*) and the earth (*erets*). What this means is that everything above and everything below were brought into existence by a miraculous act of God. It is interesting that the Hebrew *shamayim*, according to *Young's Analytical Concordance*, has a root that means "heaved up things." Whatever the understanding of the ancients might have been, today it is clear that the expanding universe fits such a description.

If the *shamayim* includes everything in the sky, this includes the sun, moon, and the stars. Someone might argue that these objects are described in verses 14 through 19, but notice that the word used in these verses is making (*asah*) not creating (*bara*). The objects were created in verse 1, the light reached the earth from these objects in verse 3, but you could not establish "signs, seasons, days and years" until verses 14 through 19. Those who argue that *bara* and *asah* mean the same thing have to invent a light for verse 3 because they claim the sun and moon came into being in verses 14–19. If we take the account literally and do not compromise the use of these words, we do not have to invent a light for verse 3. Verses 6–7 indicate that a change took place in the waters and indicates that three zones were produced—waters above the earth, water in the earth, and waters below. This is strongly suggestive of our modern understanding of hydrosphere, lithosphere, and atmosphere.

Is there any evidence to support the above description? The answer is a strong yes. First of all, we have good evidence that the universe had an explosion or expansion at its beginning that imparted an expansion to it that we see today. The age of our solar system seems to be sequentially as the Bible describes it. There is even a phenomenon that might explain the creating and making of the sun and its light. Those who have travelled in desert areas are familiar with the fact that it frequently is too hot in the desert to rain. Many times, I have seen rain fall in the Grand Canyon or the Mojave Desert and found that it evaporated before it hit the ground. If the earth was hot early in its history (and every indication is that it was) and if it tried to rain, the same thing would happen. Genesis 2:5 tells us that before there were plants and before man existed, "the LORD God had not caused it to rain upon the earth."

If the water cannot exist on the surface of the earth, where will the water be? The only place cool enough for water to exist in a stable form thermodynamically would be the atmosphere. If that volume of water is in the atmosphere, there are heavy clouds and you would not be able to establish "signs, seasons, days, and years."

There is a perfect fit between those few things that the Bible does say and what the evidence shows. This is also true in the sequence of life.

We emphasize the word *sequence* in this discussion. The chart in Appendix 8 (page 213) gives a listing of the words used in the Genesis account and what those words generally apply to. There is also an indication of how many times the words are used. As you look down the list, you will notice that all of the animals described are familiar. The word *behemah*, for example, always refers to an ungulate and is rendered *cattle* in most translations. The clearest way to see the accuracy of the sequence that is given in the biblical record is to look at the order Genesis gives. The reader might wish to begin by looking at our discussion of Genesis 1:1–3 on page 118. After these events, verses 6–10 tell us that the physical earth was modified. There is no indication of creation here—only modification. Before life could exist on the earth, there had to be an environment that could support life.

We have already made reference to the division of the waters vertically. There is also a reference to the division of waters horizontally. Verses 9–10 tell us that land and water were separated, and that the water was in one place and the dry land was in another. Every geological evidence we have indicates that this is true. The current situation of many bodies of water and many land masses is the result of this change. A casual look at the edges of North and South America, Europe, Africa, and the range of mountains in the center of the Atlantic Ocean called the Mid-Atlantic Ridge shows them all to be roughly parallel. If you take a pair of scissors and cut all of the land masses out along their continental shelves, you can actually fit them together like a jigsaw puzzle. Rocks on opposing shorelines usually match, and measurements from space and on the earth tell us that they are still moving today. (The reader may feel that Genesis 10:25 describes this process too, but it is our persuasion that this refers to the division of the languages and not the division of the land masses.)

The Bible then tells us about the *sequence* of the formation of plants. The first living thing we are told about was grass. The Hebrew here is *deshe* and the word literally means tender grass. This is not the grass you mow with your lawn mower; that word is *chat-*

sir. Tender grass is described as being easily broken. The second plant material produced in the *sequence* is the herb from the word *eseb*. A former student of mine who is Jewish tells me that, in his understanding, this word referred to a plant without hard seeds—a spore bearing plant, for example. That cannot be proven, but it is a different thing than the "herb yielding seed after his kind, and the tree yielding fruit, whose seed was in itself." This is a clear reference to an angiosperm—a tree with fruit and seed—not a fern or a grass. It seems that there are three kinds of plants given in the biblical *sequence*—the tender grass, the herb, and the flowering tree with fruit in itself. I am sure that any student of botany reading this paragraph has recognized the process of succession.

This *sequence* is something that God has created and used over and over in the history of this planet, and it still takes place today. My brothers and I own a fishing camp in Canada. Many years ago there was a terrible forest fire that burned the area right down to bed rock so that not a blade of grass nor a crumb of organic material remained. The area has recovered over the years. The first several years, there were mosses and lichens that covered the rocks in some of the shaded places. These simple plants certainly fit the description of "tender grass." In one place the moss grew so thick that, when you walked on it, you sank deep into it; and you could lie down on it and it would seem like a thick soft mattress. Eventually we began to see a few ferns, some conifers and horsetail beginning to grow in places where the mosses and lichens had accumulated enough organic material to enable the gymnosperms to grow. These certainly fit the definition of herb given in the Bible. In the following years, we have seen aspen, oaks, and birch trees starting to grow where the gymnosperms had established a base for them. This succession is in exact accord with what happened in the primitive earth, and it continues to take place today.

The *sequence* of the Bible continues to flow in exact accordance with the evidence seen in the fossils. Animal life begins in water, and in the Genesis account, the Hebrew suggests that a wide range of swarming creatures began in the sea. The fossil record confirms this, with every phylum of life known to man being found in the earliest rocks—even backboned animals. Geologists have undoubtedly taken neo-Darwinism as the basis of the theory that life started out with one-celled organisms, and that as time progressed life progressed through the familiar tree of evolution (figure 10.1, page 134). The last thing to be produced in the tree model are backboned animals, with our own species being an advanced example. The fact of the matter is that there are backboned animals in the earliest rocks, seen in the graptolite (an index fossil for the Cambrian period), the acorn worm, the lancelet, and other forms.

We also see other examples of the *sequence* accuracy of the Bible in other forms. According to the Bible, the first warm-blooded creatures were the birds. In the fossil record, we see the *archaeopteryx*, *protoavis*, and several finds recently in China backing the biblical statement. Mammals are described next, with man being the last thing to be described in the Bible. The biblical *sequence* agrees with the fossil *sequence*; and since the Bible is not attempting to give us the time of these events, we can only be impressed with its accuracy and integrity. It is interesting that evolutionary models come and go, with one of the more recent of these being punctuated equilibrium. Yet with all of this change in scientific theories, the Bible from the beginning has given a model that still stands as credible with all available scientific evidence.

When I was an atheist, I was in the process of writing a book titled *All the Stupidity of the Bible*. I taught myself Hebrew, went back to Genesis 1:1 in the original manuscripts, and attempted to show that the biblical account was pure garbage. What I ran into were the kinds of things that we have discussed. I finally gave up after almost seven years of trying to prove the Bible wrong, and decided that the Bible was credible and that I needed to look into what being a Christian was all about. I would recommend that same step to you.

WHAT ABOUT DINOSAURS?

The one remaining question in our study of the Genesis account is the question of how prehistoric creatures like the dinosaurs fit into the Genesis account. Before tackling this subject, it is important to present an explanation of our approach to the words of Genesis. It is our belief that, in order to have any meaningful understanding of the Bible, we must understand words to always have the same meaning unless there is an unquestionably unique reason why they do not (such as the biblical writer redefining a term). A New Testament example might be useful. What does the word baptize mean? Greek scholars tell me the word is derived from a Greek term meaning to immerse. In Acts 8:38, people went down into the water and John was said to be baptizing in the Jordan River "because there was much water there" (John 3:23). There are many places where there is no way to tell from the description whether the method of baptism was by sprinkling or pouring or some other method. If the word baptize is clear in most cases, I assume it must mean the same thing in all the other places. Those who maintain that there are innumerable interpretations of the Bible do so primarily because they have refused to recognize the consistency of words in the biblical account. Much of the confusion about the Genesis account among people in the religious world has taken place because words are not used consistently.

What do words like *behemah*, *kanaph*, *remes*, etc., in Genesis mean? If you look at Appendices 7 and 8 (pages 201 and 211, respectfully) you can see these words being used. I suggest that these words are used in Genesis the same way they are elsewhere in the biblical record. Behemah is used 51 times in the Bible. All of the times outside of Genesis that the word's use can be determined, it is used in reference to an ungulate—an animal that nurses its young. (The reference usually is to a cow.) What does *behemah* mean in Genesis 1:24–25? Can it refer to a *Tyranosaurus rex*? To be facetious, I seriously doubt that anyone has ever attempted to milk a *T. rex*! *Behemah* cannot refer to a dinosaur. In Job 40:15, there is another reference to a large version of *behemah*. A giant ground sloth is a real possibility for the meaning of this word, but a dinosaur is not unless the words are being used in a very inconsistent way! The *leviathan* of Job 40 is described in Psalm 104 as a creature of the deep ocean. Dinosaurs were not deep ocean creatures. The context of the passage is the struggle between good and evil, and the language certainly gives us a vivid picture of evil. Most dinosaurs were harmless cocker spaniel-sized reptiles. Words like *behemoth* and *leviathan* cannot be dinosaurs. All of the animals in Genesis 1 are animals that Moses was familiar with—his cattle, his poultry, etc.

It is a major error to assume that these words can include the amoeba, virus, duck-billed platypus, echidnas, bats, etc. There have been some 26 million different species of living things that have existed on this planet. If Genesis used half a verse to tell us about each of these, the Genesis account would be 13 million verses long and you would need a fork lift to pick up your Bible. That is not the purpose for which the Bible was written! Genesis is saying two things: (1) that God created everything and (2) that God created man special in His image. When, where, how, and why are not spelled out and are not relevant to the purposes for which the Bible was written. God has not told us when the dinosaurs were created. Like a lot of things, dinosaurs were created for a reason, fulfilled that reason, and then disappeared.

There are several possible ways to explain the dinosaurs and how they fit into Genesis. The Bible says that God does not do anything in vain (Isaiah 45:18), and that is true of the dinosaurs. There is considerable evidence that the dinosaurs were major influences in the preparation of the earth for man. The dinosaur ate gymnosperms—spore-bearing plants like ferns, conifers, etc. You and I eat angiosperms—plants with fruit and seeds, not gymnosperms. The whole dinosaur ecosystem led to the successful preparing of the earth for man to be able to live and eat. If the dinosaurs were created for this purpose, then they must have been brought into existence by God in verses 1–3 of Genesis 1. The word translated earth in Genesis 1:1 does not refer to a blob of gook in the rest of the Bible—it refers to a functioning, life-bearing planet. The word *was* in Genesis 1:2 is translated *became* in Genesis 19:26. Whether this has reference to the asteroid collision mentioned earlier is problematical, but the eradication of the dinosaurs by some process cleared the way for man and his world. The prehistory of the earth is in Genesis 1:1–3, while man and his world are created in what may have been a literal week, and man and his animals occupy the rest of the chapter.

The Bible not only gives us an account which is checkable in every detail of the history that it gives, but also a checkable means of taxonomic classification. The figure 10.1 (next page) shows the well-known Tree of Evolution as it is portrayed in Chicago's Field Museum of Natural History. In this tree, the oldest and simplest

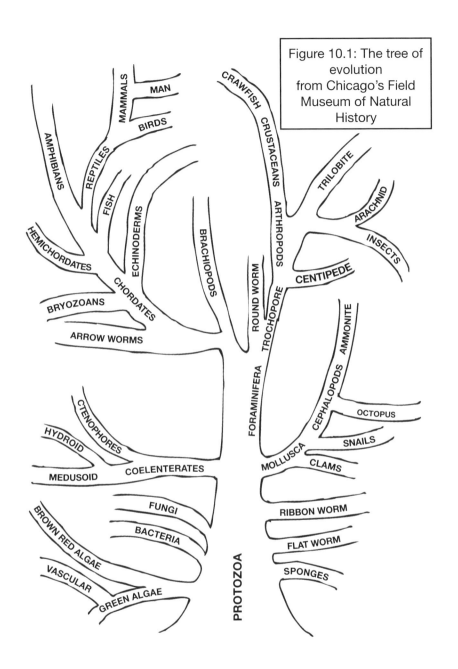

Figure 10.1: The tree of evolution from Chicago's Field Museum of Natural History

forms of life are found at the bottom of the tree, and the more complex and the more recent forms of life are at the top. There are a number of problems with this model. Animals like the trilobite have been placed at the top of this tree. This has been done because the

The Source • 133

animal is so complex. The trilobite eye is sometimes referred to as nature's most perfect eye. The eye of the trilobite was so good that it could look at something a foot away and something a mile away and they would both be in focus at the same time. Needless to say, this is not something that you and I can do. The problem with this is that the trilobite is one of the oldest animals to have ever lived on the earth. The trilobite is an index fossil for the Cambrian period which is the period when life began. There is no way this complex animal can logically be at the bottom of the evolutionary tree; so even though it is very old, it is placed near the top of the tree in the museum chart. Other examples exist that have similar problems. The bryozoans are one of the simplest animals to have ever lived on the earth, but they are not found in the earliest rocks. There are a large number of cases like these that violate the assumptions of neo-Darwinism.

There is also the problem of the ease with which animals can be classified. Classical evolutionary neo-Darwinism suggests that there should have been a large number of transitional forms between groups. These would have been animals that could not be classified easily, because they were an evolutionary "experiment" between orders or phyla. There should have been thousands of evolutionary dead ends—animals who were unsuccessful and died out, but were links between related taxonomic groups. What could you have that would be in between the cold-blooded animals and the warm-blooded animals? Can we logically believe in lukewarm-blooded animals? Rather than engage in a running gun battle, both scientists and more open creationists have looked at other options. An option suggested about 40 years ago by Dr. G. A. Kerkut in his book *Implications of Evolution* involves a forest model instead of a tree model. Another name that has been applied to this model in recent years is the lawn of evolution.

The concept being proposed here is that life started in many different trees of evolution. Each tree started independently, but the changes in the tree eventually led to a diverse population of animals who were uniquely linked. Dr. John Bonner commented on Kerkut's suggestion by saying "This is a book with a disturbing message. It points to some cracks in the foundations. The truth of the matter is that we do not know whether the transition from nonliving to living occurred once or twice or many times ... " (*American Scientist*, volume 49, June 1961, page 240 and *Scientific American*, November, 1992, page 84). The really interesting thing about this model is that it is extremely close to what the Genesis account has been saying all along. The word kind in Hebrew is the word *min*, and it is a broad term. In the New Testament 1 Corinthians 15:39 says that there are four kinds of flesh — the flesh of birds, the flesh of beast, the flesh of fish, and the flesh of man. The same system of classification is used in the first chapter of Genesis and in the flood chapter. We would suggest that the biological community has finally caught up with Genesis and that this division matches the fossil record better than any model that has ever been proposed.

Chapter 11

WHAT IS MAN?

So God created man in his own image, in the image of God he created him; male and female he created them (Genesis 1:27).

The LORD God formed the man from the dust of the ground and breathed into his nostrils the breath of life, and the man became a living being (Genesis 2:7).

In these two succinct verses, Genesis describes the unique position of humans in God's arrangement. Humans alone are created in the image of God, and only humans receive the breath of life directly from God. Humans are not unique, however, in the formation of their bodies, because they share the dust of the ground with the animals (Genesis 2:19).

For thousands of years, believers in the Genesis account of creation have not been as concerned about the literal meaning of these words as we are today. Some may have occasionally wondered: Does being made in the image of God mean that we look like God physically? Does being made from the dust of the ground mean that we are made of literal dust, or does it mean that our physical bodies are made of elements taken from the earth? Did God form

Adam as a sculptor would form a human shape from clay and then miraculously transform the clay figure into flesh and blood?

Today, however, these questions become more significant in light of scientific discoveries made over the past hundred years. The Darwinian theory of evolution has raised challenging questions about the very definition of man. Ancient bones and partial skeletons have been unearthed and pieced together to give a picture of humanlike creatures roaming the earth long before the creation of Adam. These creatures are called Hominids.

INTERPRETING THE EVIDENCE

When we combine these discoveries with improved dating techniques, Christians are finding it increasingly more difficult to summarily dismiss all the recent evidence as fictitious and unreliable. On the other hand, to blindly accept every claim made by paleoanthropologists regarding the "evolution of man" would be to ignore the sometimes scanty nature of their findings. Blind acceptance can also result in a failure to recognize hidden political agendas, which have been known to influence the interpretation of fossil finds. So before we define "man" and compare our definition with the series of creatures we see depicted in biology textbooks, we should first consider some of the problems inherent in identifying a so-called missing link between humans and animals.

Reconstructing Forms

To begin with, suppose you were to find the skeleton shown in figure 11.1 completely assembled, without any missing bones. What kind of a reconstruction could you make of the animal from which the skeleton came? Could you identify the detail shown in figure 11.2? Certainly, you could tell about how big the animal was, something about how it stood and moved, and perhaps what it ate and how it managed to survive.

However, the size of the nose, the amount of head and body hair, the shape and size of the ears would all have to be reconstructed by guesswork. Surely, no one finding a skeleton of a proboscis monkey as shown in figure 11.3 (page 140) would guess that it possessed such a large nose.

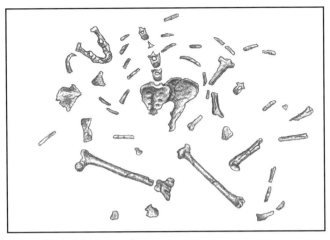

Figure 11.1: A baboon skeleton   Drawing by Katherine Cody Kicklighter

Figure 11.2: An artist's concept of pliopithecus.

Drawing by Katherine Cody Kicklighter

As far as head and body hair is concerned, the tendency is to show less of it so a proposed missing link would look more like a human. Yet since many of the creatures depicted lived in cold climates and since there is no evidence that they wore clothes, the likelihood that they had a covering of insulating body hair is very high. Calling attention to these distinctions is important, because much of the evidence presented to support evolution as a proven

Figure 11.3: Proboscis monkey

Drawing by Katherine Cody Kicklighter

"fact" has been established by the kinds of reconstructions we have just discussed.

On some occasions, scientists have presented extensive reconstructions based upon only one tooth. Sometimes these imaginative renditions have held up under further scrutiny. Other times they have not, as in the case of the Nebraskan man. This "man" was reconstructed upon the basis of a single tooth, which later turned out to be a molar from a giant wart hog (Goldschmidt 1940, 84–89). Although the scientific community has been honest in acknowledging its mistake regarding the Nebraskan man, the example is particularly noteworthy when we consider that its original proposed existence was used dramatically in court to support the theory of evolution in the now famous Scopes monkey trial held in 1925.

Since time and further research can either verify or dismiss imaginative representations of fossil finds, obviously all reconstructed forms are not automatically genuine proof of man's apparent evolution. Caution, therefore, should be exercised when we are asked to accept other, more radical claims about the evolution of humans based upon very recent finds. It takes time to conduct a proper investigation. Prehistoric events must be inferred indirectly from archaeological excavations, where the available evidence relating to prehistoric people is rare and often fragmented.

Establishing Reliable Dates

There is also the problem of establishing reliable dates for some fossils, because modern dating methods do not give good results for the critical period ranging from 50,000 to 500,000 years ago. As a result, less reliable relative dating methods may be used to cover this time period. So when we see conflicting interpretations founded upon such questionable evidence, it is wise to withhold acceptance until more proof becomes available. Drawing hard and fast conclusions based on insufficient evidence is not in accord with the scientific method.

We also need to be reminded that economics can influence interpretations of evidence. The business of finding old fossils is very competitive. A great deal of grant money for research frequently depends upon the age of the bones unearthed. The older, the better. Though it does not happen often, occasionally there have been serious disputes regarding the ages and classifications of fossils. The disputes appear to be motivated more by economic or personal factors than by the actual evidence involved (Tattersall 1995, 230), as the book *Bones of Contention* well illustrates (Lewin 1987, 195). Consequently, archaeological sites that are assigned unusually old dates should be questioned until more information becomes available.

Distinguishing between Lumpers and Splitters

Disputes about the classification of fossils are not always due to a race for commercial funding. Whether an illustration of the evolution of man shows a series of intermediate life forms connecting two different species or simply shows a gap between them very often depends upon the philosophy of the classifier. Some are "lumpers" and others are "splitters."

Definition of Race

Louis Leakey was a leader in the splitter camp. Every time he found a part of a primate in the stratum he was studying, he gave it a new name. Those of the lumper camp, however, lumped many of these new forms into already existing groups. They suggested that the numerous fossils Leakey had found were merely different races of the same species of animal.

At this point, it might be helpful to explain what is meant by the term "race." A race is a group of individuals possessing a physical characteristic chosen by the observer as a basis for identification. For example, a teacher could decide to segregate students into three racial groups according to the size of their earlobes, whether they are long, intermediate, or short.

Some who think skin color is the only determining factor for racial prejudice might object to this rather peculiar use of the word. We prefer skin color as a criterion for separating the races because we choose to do so. As a matter of convenience, we need an obvious, prejudicial characteristic that is readily identifiable. Skin color is obvious and is identifiable at fifty yards. Electing to examine an earlobe to distinguish between those we will accept from those we will not could be awkward, to say the least, and would probably be much harder to sell socially.

Example of Racial Variations

How do racial variations come about in real life? The earlobe illustration can answer that question. Earlobe size has been a function of social custom at various times in the past. A certain group may have felt that people with long earlobes were witches and needed to be executed to protect society. As a result, eventually everyone remaining alive would have short earlobes because according to the rules of heredity, children would generally look like their parents.

Conversely, in another culture, long earlobes may have been a sign of beauty or virility. A person with such a distinguished characteristic could hang jewelry on the earlobes and be more attractive than average. This would mean that such people would probably marry sooner, have more children, and thus increase the number of people in the community with long earlobes. Subsequently, two races (based upon earlobes) would come into existence by a very natural process. The intermediate earlobe would be formed, perhaps, by interracial marriages between the other two earlobe types.

Application to Microevolution

If we understand this definition of racial differences, we can appreciate the problem inherent in a lineup of humanlike animals illustrating how man is supposed to have gradually changed over a long period of time. Do the changes in form represent separate species that required macroevolution? Or are they simply racial variations within the same species, meaning that only microevolution has been taking place?

For example, the average size of a male Japanese skull prior to World War II was just over 900 cubic centimeters, whereas today the average size is 1,400 cubic centimeters. Since brain size is proportional to body size and modern Japanese males are significantly taller today, the increase in brain size can be attributed simply to improved nutrition.

If splitters were to unearth skulls with such differences in size as the ones just described, they could easily assume that two separate species of creatures were represented. On that basis, they could go on to erroneously use them as examples of several "missing links" between apes and humans. Lumpers, on the other hand, would see the increase in brain size as merely a racial variation of the same species, a change well within the limits set by natural adaptation and not, therefore, an example of macroevolution at all.

For this reason, we should use caution when weighing the evidence for newfound links in the so-called evolutionary chain. Being cautious, however, does not mean automatic rejection. We do not want to imply that all research done in tracing hominid-like creatures through the fossil record is erroneous.

Quite the contrary, the argument that the human body may have evolved and the search for evidence to validate that claim are examples of how we are able to advance in knowledge and technology. Without proposing theories, right or wrong, and searching for data to substantiate them, we would still be living in the Dark Ages.

We have mentioned these problems to show that it would be deceptive to state as a fact that humans are solely a product of evolution when it is obvious that grave difficulties are inherent in that position. Nevertheless, an honest consideration of the research on evolution has caused many Christians to discover how God may have used microevolution as a part of his creative process.

Creature without a Soul

This distinction between human and instinctual behavior is important in dealing with some of the hard-to-answer questions associated with the so-called history of man. The fossil evidence strongly suggests that long before God created Adam and Eve, he created a number of other humanlike animals that, as we have said, have been classified as hominids. These creatures had smaller brains that were apparently preprogrammed by instinct to perform a number of needed survival skills, but the creatures did not display any of the unique characteristics that reflect a spiritual makeup. This is a fact that is not disputed by science.

An instinctive animal like this would live from day to day by means of its preprogrammed routines and remember new things (store additional information) for survival purposes only. It would not remember daily events contextually. Even today, it is observed that "monkeys employ rule-like strategies for promoting the welfare of a group, including maintaining peace, observing boundaries, and sharing food. And they abide by these rules without necessarily understanding them" (Hauser 2000, 55). This is an example of microculture.

Stone Tools

The expression, "Monkey see, monkey do," arises because monkeys are recognized as being capable of mimetic behaviors (mimicking) without knowing what they are doing or why. While some paleoanthropologists see the making of tools as being a purely human ability, others disagree.

Colin Renfrew of the McDonald Institute for Archaeological Research in Cambridge, England, states:

An alternative view [to human toolmakers] is that the Lower and Middle Paleolithic do indeed represent a "mimetic" phase, and that the production of well-defined tool forms does not require any very sophisticated conceptualizing

> ### The Difference between Micro- and Macroculture
>
> *The word* culture *has a variety of definitions, depending upon the dictionary consulted. More modern dictionaries exclusively associate culture with human behavior. However, older dictionaries broadly define* culture *as being "any learned behavior that is not inherited by instinct." Within this broad definition, many animals qualify as being cultural because their parents teach them certain behaviors. Unless the reader knows the difference, confusion can result when culture is associated with the behavior of an animal, such as a chimpanzee.*
>
> *In this discussion, we will view culture the same way we view evolution. Just as micro- and macroevolution reflect differences between small and large changes in physical attributes, so micro- and macro-acculturation (the acquisition of culture) would reflect similar differences between simple (small) and complex (large) cultural behavior changes.*
>
> *Many animals display micro- or simple acculturation when* culture *is defined as any "behavior that is socially taught, rather than instinctive"* (Scott, Foresman Advanced Dictionary, 1993). *However, only humans display macro-acculturation, defined as being "the totality of socially transmitted behavior patterns, arts, beliefs, institutions, and all other products of human work and thought. These patterns, traits, and products [are] considered with respects to a particular category, such as field, subject, or mode of expression; [for example] religious culture in the Middle Ages; musical culture; oral culture"* (American Heritage Talking Dictionary; Copyright 1997, The Learning Company, Inc.).

power. Moreover such conceptualization as was needed need not have been language dependent (1998,177–178).

The early prehuman toolmakers were nothing more than instinctual animals with a wide range of built-in skills that were transmitted through mimicry, without the necessity of human intelligence.

A brief look at the stone "tools" used by these animals supports this view. Normally, when we hear the term "stone tools" or "stone tool industry," we picture a tool pouch loaded with a neat array of rock tools, possibly resembling Native American arrowheads or knife blades that are excellently crafted and obviously the work of skilled specialists. This is not the case, however, with the stone tools associated with early hominid fossils.

The hominid tools were crude and, in their original setting, would be hard to distinguish from naturally broken rocks. In fact, when the science of classifying stone tools was first introduced, a difficult period followed when many naturally broken rocks were ambitiously categorized as being tools (Tattersall 1998, 128). Many of the specimens that are classified as "hand axes" are nothing more than two hand-sized stones that were struck together to produce a single-sided, sharp edge. Such altered rocks and their flakes are frequently found scattered randomly around a site. If a natural cause for the damaged rocks cannot be envisioned, then it is assumed that a hominid did the work, whether any evidence of a hominid is found there or not. Of the tens of thousands of broken stones classified as being over one million years old, fewer than a dozen have been objectively assigned an actual use (Jones et al. 1992, 328).

When hominids did use these tools, there is no indication that they treated them any differently than ordinary rocks. Apparently, when the animals needed something to cut with, they looked around until they found a suitable sharp stone flake. If one was not available, they may have bashed two rocks together until one chipped off.

The chipped-off flakes may have been used as crude blades held between the first two fingers. When the creature finished using it, the blade was dropped without particular notice. So, pragmatically, we might not even think of these as real tools in the modern sense. They were just convenient items that were used when needed and abandoned when not. (See figure 11.4 for an illustration of how stone tools have changed over time.)

Yet despite this uncertainty about the tool's formation and use, the hominids believed to have made them are referred to as being human and classified as *Homo*. In many cases, this classification is deceptive because the creatures were no more human than trained

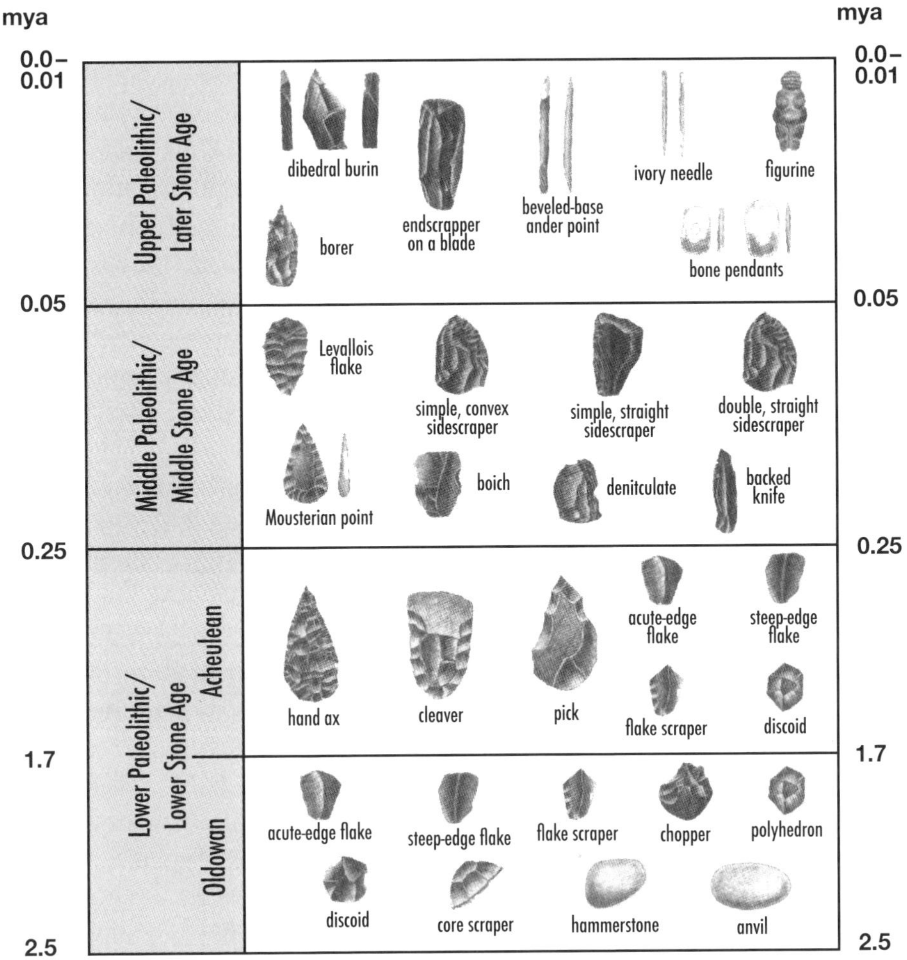
mya
0.0–
0.01
0.05
0.25
1.7
2.5
Upper Paleolithic/
Later Stone Age
Middle Paleolithic/
Middle Stone Age
Lower Paleolithic/
Lower Stone Age
Acheulean
Oldowan
dibedral burin
endscrapper
on a blade
beveled-base
ander point
ivory needle
figurine
borer
bone pendants
Levallois
flake
simple, convex
sidescraper
simple, straight
sidescraper
double, straight
sidescraper
Mousterian point
boich
denitculate
backed
knife
acute-edge
flake
steep-edge
flake
hand ax
cleaver
pick
flake scraper
discoid
acute-edge flake
steep-edge flake
flake scraper
chopper
polyhedron
discoid
core scraper
hammerstone
anvil

From *The Human Career: Human Biological and Cultural Origin* by R. G. Klein. ©1999 The University of Chicago Press. Used by permission. Tool drawings by Katherine Cody Kicklighter

Figure 11.4: How stone tools have changed over time

chimpanzees. Today groups of chimpanzees are known to accumulate tool-like debris at their sites similar to the stone "hammers" found on ancient hominid sites (Jones et al. 1992, 326).

Based upon this evidence, we can conclude that if a hominid did not demonstrate image-of-God characteristics, it would be an animal. Such an animal could never be classified as being a person as we understand the word.

DEFINING *MAN* ANTHROPOLOGICALLY

Making this distinction is important because when asking for a scientific definition of man, a person is likely to get a variety of responses, depending upon the specialty of the scientist queried. The definition has particular relevance because of the popularization of physical anthropology in books such as *National Geographic* and/or the *Time-Life* series on the evolution of man. Through these publications, the names Leakey, Johnson, White, Dubois, and Goodall have become well known in the United States. The research of these scientists has led to what can be called the "caveman complex," which asserts that man's evolutionary descent from tree-dwelling apes has been proven as scientific fact.

The supposed evolutionary progress of man has been depicted as a line of advancing body shapes starting from a small lemur and ending with modern man. Because pictures and exhibits like these are found in many museums and schools, the message is that the lineup is based upon discovered evidence in the fossil record. In the past, those who believed in the biblical account of creation have shown that the evidence does not support such a simplistic view. It appears now that the facts are finally winning out. Hublin, paraphrasing a portion of a book by anthropologist Richard G. Klein, says, "The once-popular fresco showing a single file of marching Hominids becoming ever more vertical, tall and hairless now appears to be a fiction" (2000, 263).

Though the author writes from an evolutionist's perspective, his honesty allows us to be encouraged by his findings. To investigate the matter further, we need to decide what the words man and human really mean when applied to hominid fossils.

Physical Attributes vs. Soul

In figure 11.5, we see a list of physical attributes that anthropologists tell us are unique to humans. They contend that if an animal possesses any of these traits, it may be physically and intellectually related to man. Such a creature is then often referred to in scientific circles as being "unconditionally human." A more accurate description would be "hominid-like animal," or better yet, "bipedal primate" (erect-standing, highest-order mammal).

```
   1.  A cranial capacity of 900 to 2300 cubic centimeters.
   2.  50% more nerve cells in the visual center than other animals.
   3.  A rounded skull with a vertical forehead.
   4.  Moderate supraorbital ridges.
   5.  Rounded instead of pointed occipital.
   6.  A lack of muscle ridge.
   7.  A vertical forehead.
   8.  An arched dental pattern.
   9.  A second molar behind the canine.
  10.  A 2-1-2-3 tooth pattern.
  11.  A skeleton adapted for upright locomotion.
  12.  A total dependence on learning for survival.
  13.  A totally opposable thumb.
  14.  An extreme organization of the brain.
  15.  The longest childhood dependency period.
```

Figure 11.5: Physical attributes said to be unique to humans

After reviewing these human characteristics, it will be apparent that this approach to defining man has almost nothing in common with the biblical definition we will discuss next or with relevant facts. Based upon what we will view about consciousness, is it possible that a hominid-like animal might possess all fifteen of these characteristics and yet still not have a soul? Remember, without a soul such a creature would have no self-consciousness and, therefore, would not be a person.

In tacit support of this possibility, it is now becoming apparent to leaders in the field of paleoanthropology that hominid-like bodies came into existence thousands of years before any truly "modern behavioral patterns" associated with human activity were discernible in the fossil record (Tattersall 1998, 175). Klein concurs when he states, "Together, the fossil and archaeological records suggest that the modern physical form evolved before the modern capacity for culture" (1999, 572).

Realizing this should quickly make it obvious that the starting point for the argument over the origin of man depends upon which definition of human a person is willing to accept. Literally, a caveman, biblically speaking, is a man with a soul who lives in a cave, nothing more and nothing less.

Hominids vs. Prehistoric People

The typical scientific prehistoric caveman is more accurately defined as a cave hominid. A search in any good encyclopedia will show an outline of the descent of "man" under the heading "Prehistoric People." This sequence is assumed to cover a time period from 60 million years to about 5,500 years ago when writing suddenly appeared. Starting with writing, we entered into what is called "historic" times, because we can now refer to written records as an aid in determining past events.

To avoid unnecessary confusion, we should qualify the term "prehistoric people." Most reference sources do not distinguish between animals and people, even though over 99.8% of the prehistoric period deals only with animals. To eliminate this problem, we will reserve such terms as *people* and *human* to refer only to descendants of Adam created in the image of God.

All other humanlike creatures will be recognized as being animals and called either by their taxonomic names or by their general family name, Hominidae. A hominid, simply put, is a higher order mammal that has a basically similar skeleton to that of a human. The three other distinguishing features of hominids have to do with the size of brain and teeth and the flatness of face. Most animal faces are not flat. Animals have snouts that project out from their faces (prognathism), leaving them chinless.

Modern apes are not considered to be hominids. In scientific circles, it is clearly recognized that they are not part of the so-called human family tree. Apes do not walk erect. They are recognized as being knuckle walkers, since they generally use their hands or fists somewhat like a four-footed animal when walking. They are in the family Pongidae.

DEFINING *MAN* BIBLICALLY

As we consider what the fossil record reveals to us about the so-called history of man, we encounter hominid-like creatures that are believed to have fashioned crude stone tools. The Bible student may wonder how these creatures fit into the Bible's description of Adam as the first man God created. Here is where we need to define what man is according to the Bible and then compare the Bible's description with the anthropological definition of man.

We find that in Genesis 1:27 and 2:7, quoted at the beginning of this chapter, a distinction is made between the way God created animals and the way he created humans. Both were made from the dust of the ground, but God made the first human in his own image and personally breathed life into him.

When the Bible uses the phrase "image of God," should that be taken to mean that humans look like God physically? Obviously not, or else we would all look identical, and God would have a physical body just like ours. Such a view would conflict with other descriptions of the Creator found in the Bible. In chapter 5 of this book, we discussed the Bible's claim that God is not flesh and blood (Matthew 16:17, KJV), God is spirit (John 4:24), and God does not have physical limitations as we do (Jeremiah 23:24; Luke 1:3). Therefore, the image of God must refer not to the physical but to the spiritual nature of humans, because spiritually we do all "look" alike.

Possession of a Soul

Such a definition enables us to see what humans really are. We are those beings who possess souls uniquely created in the image of God. We possess intellect, personality, and the ability and inclination to worship. We can be taught to reason, to feel guilt, to be sympathetic, to forgive, and to create works of art and music. All these characteristics are embodied in the concept of "culture," and it is the cultural aspects of our existence that set us apart from the animals and clearly identify us as human.

Even the most intelligent animal cannot reflect the image of God. Chimpanzees do not write protest songs or paint creative expressions of their beliefs. I have an adopted son with a measured Stanford-Binet Intelligence Quotient (IQ) of about 55. There are many porpoises and chimpanzees who are said to have intelligence quotients somewhat higher than his.

Contrast with Animals

Nevertheless, has a porpoise or chimpanzee ever expressed himself in art or music that made any sense at all? Extensive programs of instruction designed to teach these animals to do so have not had favorable results. An animal is capable of drawing nothing beyond crudely executed circles and lines randomly oriented. My son Tim, on the other hand, draws pictures showing personal sensitivity and expression. He also composes his own songs. Obviously, he does not do these things because of his intelligence. It is his spiritual makeup that makes these uniquely human traits possible.

Is it possible for a creature's environment to account for all these characteristics? If a chimpanzee were brought up in the same environment as my son, would that make a difference? A psychology professor named Dr. Winthrop Kellogg of Indiana University conducted an experiment to test this hypothesis. Later another scientist duplicated his experiment with similar results.

When Dr. Kellogg's wife, Luella, had their ten-month-old son at home, Dr. Kellogg brought a chimp home from the zoo, who was seven and a half months old (July 1931). The human (Donald) and chimp (Gua) infants were raised in identical environments and given equal stimulation, love, and education. Dr. Kellogg's hypothesis

Figure 11.6: Tim's Drawing

was that the chimpanzee would do all the things his son would do, but on a lower level because of lower intelligence. At the conclusion of his experiment (March 1932), however, Dr. Kellogg's chimp had failed to create any works of art or music or, for that matter, to demonstrate any uniquely human characteristics. It was rumored "that Donald was becoming more chimp-like than Gua human!"

Even one of the most famous of the intelligent chimpanzees, Washoe, was not able to demonstrate anything approaching human intelligence. Washoe's trainers claimed she had mastered many elements of American Sign Language, but critics have successfully argued that her humanlike actions were primarily the result of subtle clues she inadvertently received from her handlers, along with their often generous interpretation of irrelevant gestures as being words.

Thorndike has shown that pigeons given equivalent amounts of time can be conditioned to make seemingly intelligent responses as well (1978). Mark Caldwell reports, "The history of science is littered with animals that seemed to be displaying extraordinary brain

Figure 11.7: An artist's rendition of a chimpanzee drawing

power but were just responding to unconscious prompts from their owners and trainers" (2000, 73).

Humans alone possess the unique characteristics of independent, creative intelligence because they are created in the image of God. There is no workable explanation for how these intellectual abilities could have been acquired naturally, and no animal has ever been observed to manifest true human traits, even under the most favorable conditions.

The inherent desire to worship a Supreme Being is additional evidence of humanity's created nature. No matter how primitive or advanced a person might be, even if geographically isolated from traditional influences, he will eventually engage in religious practices involving supernatural powers. No animal does this consciously, regardless of how high its IQ is. Yet my mentally-retarded son, even with his low IQ, leads us in prayer, talks about God, and participates in worship.

Humans also differ from animals in their capacity to feel guilt and sympathy and in their willingness to forgive others. Sometimes we associate these qualities of guilt and forgiveness with animals, especially with our pets because we tend to anthropomorphize them (assign human feelings to them).

However much we would like them to be more like us, there is no visible evidence that a dog feels sorry for the neighbor's cat when running it up a tree, regardless of how many times this might happen. True forgiveness, while rare in adult humans, is nonexistent in animals.

When my daughter picked out a pet kitten at the humane society, I was forced, unfortunately, to pull it roughly out of a cage containing other kittens and cats. For the next eight years, every time that cat saw me, it hissed and spat, even though I fed it, petted it, and repeatedly tried to play with it. Humans can act that way, too, but the capacity to forgive and forget is also there. Animals do not possess these singularly human characteristics at all.

Instinct and Conditioning

Often what may appear to be a humanlike response can be attributed to instinct and what we call "conditioning." Instinctive commands are "hard wired" into the creature's brain and form subconscious mental pathways, often equipping the creature to perform astounding feats, such as a spider's ability to spin a complicated web. The animal or insect is not conscious of what it is doing any more than we are conscious of making our hearts beat faster when we are frightened.

Conditioning an animal to repeat instinctive behaviors is based upon the research of Russian physiologist Ivan Pavlov, wherein a trainer rewards the animal over and over again until a desired pattern of behavior emerges. Eventually, the behavior becomes ingrained in the animal's brain because of the response-reward training program.

A very interesting project showing the remarkable potential for conditioned, instinctive behavior has to do with parrots. Animal behaviorist Irene Pepperberg, who has researched animal intelligence for more than twenty years, has demonstrated that parrots can be taught to perform tricks and speak human phrases that are beyond anything they would do in their natural environment. One of the most mysterious of their talents involves the letters b and p, which we form with our lips. Nobody knows yet how a lipless parrot can form these sounds, let alone how it can so successfully imitate human speech in general (Caldwell 2000, 74).

So an animal can be trained to sound and look as if it has human characteristics, but it cannot be trained to feel the personal emotions that produce them naturally. A parrot imitates human speech, but it does not originate the thoughts behind the words.

Capacity for Language

Here is where the most significant components of a human soul made in the image of God become obvious, namely in the phenomenon of consciousness and the capacity for language. Consciousness is a metaphysical or spiritual state. Despite numerous efforts, a conscious center located somewhere in the brain has never been identified. That is because unconscious brain matter cannot produce physical consciousness any more than a computer, no matter how complex, could ever become conscious as we are (Tattersall 1998, 190–197). The state of consciousness comes from God, whether genetically or directly.

Consciousness also involves having a sense of "self" that is impossible without the capacity for language. In order to have personal memories, we must have language in which to encode them. This is more than just mental pictures. It is actual self-talk, conversations with ourselves that we remember and use to interpret our mental pictures. In order to have higher-order thought processes to subjectively qualify and quantify what is seen, heard, or felt, we need language to express those thoughts to ourselves and to others.

Despite many decades of investigation, the biological bases for consciousness and language remain a mystery. This is significant to those who believe in Divine creation because some experts in the field now theorize that the ability to use a syntactical language may have emerged rapidly as the result of a "single genetic event" (Clark 1993, 172).

So we see that the two definitions of what man is are based on different criteria. The mechanical definition of science lends itself to being able to see evidence of man's history in a physical way—brain size, bone ratios, mandible shapes, etc. Then the biblical definition involves man's soul expressed in art, music, worship, guilt, sympathy, and the ability to be taught to think. These are not exclusive of each other. We analyze a fossil and tell something of where it fits into history by the scientific definition. Our decision of what man is affects our view of our peers and how we treat each other. It is important not to relegate any human to merely animal status.

In June 2009, we had a case where people associated with PETA (People for the Ethical Treatment of Animals) got upset with then President Barak Obama when he killed a fly during an interview with a reporter from CNBC. If all you view man to be is an animal with a certain set of physical characteristics, then a fly is as valuable as a human, and killing a human is no worse than killing a bug. If man is created in the image of God then man is of greater value than any living thing no matter what his physical, social, economic, sexual, or political condition is.

The evidence not only supports the fact that humans are created in the image of God, but the logical sequences of not believing that are horrendous.

12

CONCLUSION

The case for the existence of God does not hinge upon one piece of evidence or one particular concept or one logical approach. Instead, evidence for the existence of God can be found everywhere, from the formation of matter in the cosmos to the intricacies of the human cell to the evidence for a spiritual makeup to man. Even in this lengthy discussion, we have barely scratched the surface of the handiwork of God. New discoveries come to light on a daily basis.

In this book, we have shown that it is logical and reasonable to believe that the carefully designed creation we see about us is the product of a personal God. This belief contrasts sharply with accepting the notion that the cosmos came out of mindless nothing in a series of fortuitous accidents.

In Romans 1:19–20, the concept of design is offered as a proof for God's existence. The statement is made that even the unseen things of God can be clearly understood through what he has made and created. We have demonstrated in a variety of ways—both at the intuitive level and with some mathematical analysis—that the creation could not have occurred by chance but must be the result of intelligent design. We have found that this design argument applies to every relevant scientific discipline. If there is design, then there must be a designer or planner responsible for it all.

In this regard, we are living at a very exciting period in human history. For the first time, we have peered into the living cell and have seen a complexity of design unparalleled in anything humans have ever made or dreamed of making. This complexity, appearing so early in earth's history, has left no time for a purely natural evolution of life. If such a discovery has forced some scientists to theorize that life must have come to earth from outer space, we laud that conclusion and add to it by naming the source of life and power and design—the great God of the universe.

We are also living at a time when we have "seen" the Cambrian explosion of life in the Burgess Shale and the Chengjiang fossils. Here again, the length of time available for such a diversity of complex body parts and systems to come about by natural selection, mutation, and genetic drift alone is far too short to account for "life's big bang." But the Bible describes this sudden appearance of life in earth's oceans when it says, "And God said, 'Let the water teem with living creatures'" (Genesis 1:20).

In our opinion, these two events alone—the emergence of the living cell and the Cambrian explosion—have essentially invalidated the Godless theory of evolution. Therefore, we believe the question confronting scientists today is not, "Does God exist?" but rather, "How and when did God intervene in his progressive creation to produce the complex web of life we observe all around us?" As we keep abreast of the many new discoveries coming to light almost daily on this subject, we echo the words of Henry F. Schaefer, quantum chemist and five time nominee for the Nobel Prize: "The significance and joy in my science comes in those occasional moments of discovering something new and saying to myself, 'So that's how God did it.' My goal is to understand a little corner of God's plan" (Sheler and Schrof 1991, 7).

Our goal in writing this book has been to do the same—to reveal just a small measure of God's creative power. In so doing, we have consistently turned to the Bible as his inspired Word. In the fields of medicine, astronomy, physical science, geology, and virtually every other discipline, the Bible makes statements that surpass the educational limitations of its authors. To quickly reject these statements as being due to luck or chance is not satisfying because there are just too many "chance" occurrences to account for.

For example, it is incomprehensible that a man writing 3,200 years ago could make accurate medical observations only now proven true through the use of highly sophisticated scientific equipment. The sequence of creation found in Genesis 1 is also more than coincidental. Fossil evidence has required scientists to revise their theories of evolution to agree with the Genesis account of creation. The theory of punctuated equilibrium is a compromise on the part of evolutionists in recognition of the fact that changes take place in the fossil record much faster than predicted by the evolutionary theory of uniformitarianism.

Some of the supposed contradictions between science and the Bible appear because of bad science, such as accepting the evolution of man from early primates as factual when there are valid academic arguments against the concept. Other contradictions appear because of bad theology, such as accepting the suggestions of men that the Bible can be used as a clock to establish the absolute time periods for various events in earth's history.

However, both the Bible and science agree that humans are conspicuously different from the animals that preceded them. The unique cultural endowments of humans establish them as being created in the image of God, clearly proving that we are not the product of chance but of intelligent design.

The charge that there is insufficient evidence for God's existence is plainly misleading. The problem is that many people today demand absolute proof in areas where absolute proof is not possible, unless God decides to reveal himself directly. Why is it that we humans demand far more proof when it comes to God than we do in other areas of our lives?

There is a leap of faith in nearly everything we seriously depend upon. Every Christian realizes that there are many questions relative to God, his origin, his plan, and his methods that cannot be answered completely or, in many cases, even comprehended. Nevertheless, our leap of faith need not be a blind one. Indeed, God does not require such a mindless commitment but rather asks us to leap based upon rational, understandable evidence that he has provided in abundance.

To deny God, a man or woman must ignore a great deal of favorable evidence, as we have shown. The social consequences of such denials are obvious. Realizing this, it may be that you already see the importance of acknowledging that God exists and that he cares for you (Hebrews 11:6). This will allow you to personally experience his working in your life. However, this cannot happen until you give yourself to him unconditionally.

With this in mind, we urge you to review the arguments in this book to see if they will help you to intelligently make your own leap of faith. You can do this with the assurance that both God and Jesus Christ can and will work through you for the rest of your life on this earth and into eternity.

When we discuss concepts dealing with how God may have performed his acts of creation, we are bound to raise questions in the minds of our readers. For that reason, we invite you to ask us these questions by writing to us. We would welcome the opportunity to clarify ideas or to refer you to other sources of information. To contact the author, write:

John Clayton
1555 Echo Valley Drive
Niles, MI 49120
E-mail: jncdge@aol.com

We do not have all the answers, but we have studied this material extensively. Therefore, we welcome the opportunity to be of assistance to you and to learn from you as well.

Does God Exist? family websites:
doesgodexist.org;
dandydesigns.org;
scienceterrific.org;
whypain.org; and
doesgodexist.tv

Appendix

APPENDIX A

This appendix contains three charts about accuracy in several different religions. The charts are:

> Checkable Biblical Accuracy
> Scientific Accuracy of the Book of Mormon
> Scientific Accuracy of the Koran

Checkable Biblical Accuracy

In each of the following cases the biblical writer had an opportunity to either state the widely held erroneous belief of his day, or to state a factually true description. In each case what was stated was true, demonstrating knowledge beyond the writer's ability and thus necessarily from God.

FACTS AS STATED IN BIBLE	BIBLICAL REFERENCES	COMMON BELIEF OF DAY IN WHICH AUTHOR LIVED
Blood is essential to life.	Leviticus 17:11–14	Disease and spirits reside in blood. To cure disease, bleed patient.
Both male and female possess "seed of life."	Genesis 3:15; 22:18	Male has baby in him. Woman is the incubator.
Eating blood of animals forbidden.	Leviticus 17:12, 14	Raw blood used as beverage.

FACTS AS STATED IN BIBLE	BIBLICAL REFERENCES	COMMON BELIEF OF DAY IN WHICH AUTHOR LIVED
Do not eat animals that died naturally.	Leviticus 17:15	No restrictions on manner of death.
Quarantine of certain diseases.	Leviticus 13–15	No isolation of diseased.
Do not eat pork, scavengers (in Moses' day).	Leviticus 11	No food restrictions.
Principles of avoiding bacterial contamination—one person to another.	Leviticus 15:19–33	No rules of hygiene or isolation.
Human waste products to be buried.	Deuteronomy 23:12–14	Human waste left on ground.
Human body can be opened for surgery.	Genesis 2:21	First operations done secretly because populace threatened doctors.
Burning clothes, washing self after contact with deceased man or animal.	Numbers 19:5–22	No recognition of contagion problem.
Earth is round, day and night taking place simultaneously.	Isaiah 40:22 Proverbs 8:27 Luke 17:34	Earth is flat.
Earth is not physically supported.	None mentioned and Job 26:7	Earth held up by four elephants or Atlas (a man), etc.
The North is empty (our North Pole points out of the galaxy).	Job 26:7	Seeing a few stars to the North refuted this idea until 1932.
Space and stars are too large to be measured.	Genesis 15:5 Jeremiah 33:22	Attempts to number the astronomical bodies went on until 1932.
The creation sequence—plants, water creatures, birds, mammals, man, in that order.	Genesis 1:11–28	Most had man first. All varied from correct concept.

FACTS AS STATED IN BIBLE	BIBLICAL REFERENCES	COMMON BELIEF OF DAY IN WHICH AUTHOR LIVED
The age of everything in the creation is the same.	Genesis 1:1	Different times for different objects.
The continents have floated away from a singular original land mass.	Genesis 1:9	Each continent was autonomous (until 1970).
Herbert Spencer's scientific principles.	Genesis 1	No scientific system of statements.
Lightning is produced naturally.	Jeremiah 10:13; 51:16	Gods throw lightning bolts.
All men are blood relatives.	Acts 17:26	Men have different origins.
The water cycle.	Ecclesiastes 1:7 Job 36:27, 28	Gods pour new water on land continuously.
Use of genetics in livestock.	Genesis 30:30–43	No recognition of inherited physical properties.
Snow and ice seen as valuable.	Job 38:22	Snow and ice seen as a scourage and waste.
Seaworthy ratio for ship construction—30x5x3.	Genesis 6:15	Ships ratio not considered; only the beauty.
Concepts of id and ego.	Romans 7	God induced behavior explanations.
Animals can be changed (mutated).	Genesis 3:14	No change possible.
Directional correctness.	Luke 10:30	Directional error.
Distance accuracy.	Luke 24:13	Errors in distance.

The Scientific Accuracy of
the Book of Mormon

MORMON CONCEPT	FACT
Burying swords in the earth will keep them bright (unrusted) (Alma 24:16).	Burying swords will accelerate their rusting.
Leprosy occurred in the Americas in A.D. 34 (III Nephi 17:7).	The first known case of leprosy in the Americas was in 1758.
Indians had many official records (Helaman 3:15), scrolls (Mormon 5:23), and other writings (Mormon 9:2; III Nephi 9:18; 12:18).	The Indians wrote no books and used only simple picture writing.
God cursed the Indians with dark skin and anyone who marries an Indian "shall be cursed with the same cursing" (II Nephi 5:21; Jacob 3:3–9; Mormon 5:15–17; II Nephi 5:23; Alma 3:6–10).	If this were true, there would be no part Indians, only full Indians. The statement is genetically false.
When Indians accept the Mormon teachings, they will become "a white and delightsome people" (II Nephi 30:5–7; III Nephi 2:15).	No case histories. In fact such a change would imply a correlation between goodness and degree of whiteness.
Baldness is caused by sin (II Nephi 13:24)	Baldness is hereditary or chemically caused.
Domestic cattle, oxen, and cows are separate species, all present in the Americas when man came here (Ether 9:18–19).	They are all the same species and were not in the Americas when man arrived here.

MORMON CONCEPT	FACT
Numerous people and animals in North America were exterminated by poisonous snakes, with sheep driven to the south by the snakes who cooperated with each other. The people ate the animals that had been killed by the snakes (Ether 9:30–34).	There are very few poisonous snakes in North America. Going south increases the probability of contact with snakes. Snakes do not cooperate. There would be too many dead animals for the people to have eaten them, and this would have been against Jewish dietary laws anyway.
Lions are beasts of the forests (III Nephi 20: 16; 21:12).	Lions live in the savannahs, not in the forests.
Silk was produced in the Americas (I Nephi 13:7; Alma 4:6; Ether 9:17; 10:24).	Silk was and is produced in Asia, at that time exclusively.
Indians used butter, honey, and candles (II Nephi 17:15; III Nephi 8:21).	These items were unknown to the Indians and were introduced by Europeans after Columbus.
Disease is caused by climate (Alma 46:40).	Disease is not caused by climate.
Arabia has much fruit and honey (I Nephi 17:5).	Arabia is a desert and has been for many thousands of years.
Jews made ships from the "ample timber of Arabia" (I Nephi 18:1).	There are very few trees in Arabia and none useable for ship building.

MORMON CONCEPT	FACT
Nephi and other faithful Jews left the "Land of Jerusalem" to go to North America where they planted seeds they had brought. "These seeds grew exceedingly." The claimed date is 591 B.C. (I Nephi 18:24; Mosiah 9:9; Jacob 5:1).	Crops of the Near East were olives, wheat, barley, figs, dates, onions, pomegranates, and peaches. Crops from the Americas were potatoes, tobacco, blueberries, cranberries, eggplants, and maize (corn). There is no support for early European crops being the start of American crops.
The Arabia river named Laman flows continually into the Red Sea (I Nephi 2:6–9).	There are no rivers at all in Arabia flowing into the Red Sea nor have there been in human history.
North America has cows, oxen, asses, and horses (I Nephi 18:25).	There were no cows, horses, or asses in North America when it was discovered.
Jared and his family kept all species of fish that inhabit the Americas alive in aquaria for 344 days (Ether 6:1). He also brought these as well as birds, bees, and seed which populated North America (Ether 2:2–3; 5:4).	American birds and fish are for the most part different than those of the Old World. There are very few species of any of these forms that are the same on both continents.
Native language of the Hebrews between 600 B.C. and 91 B.C. was Egyptian (I Nephi 1:2; Mosiah 1:4). Mormon 9:32 refers to "Reformed Egyptian" around A.D. 400.	The Hebrews spoke Hebrew in 600 B.C. Due to the Babylonian Captivity from 560 to 538 B.C. Aramaic became the language. Reformed Egyptian is unknown.

MORMON CONCEPT	FACT
Plant grafting was done in the Americas between 600 B.C. and A.D. 421. (I Nephi 15:16; Jacob 5)	Grafting was not practiced by the Indians.
Leopards, asps, cockatrices were present in North America (II Nephi 21:6–8, 30:12–14).	None of these animals are native to North America.

From "A Biologist Examines the Book of Mormon" by Thomas D. S. Key, *Journal of the American Scientific Affiliation*, June 1985, pages 96–99.

The Scientific Accuracy of the Koran

REFERENCE	STATEMENT	FACT
Al-Nahl 16:66 (Sura of the Bee)	Excretion, blood, and milk come from cattle's abdomen.	Milk and excretion come from different parts of the cow's anatomy.
Al-Nahl 16:69 (Sura of the Bee)	Honey comes out of a bee's abdomen and heals men.	Honey is not produced in a bee's abdomen.
Al-Anam 6:38 (Sura of the Cattle)	All animals and all things that fly form communities like man.	Many forms of life do not live in communities.
Al-Saffat 37:6 (The Ranks) to Al-Jinn 72:8–9 (The Spirits) Al-Tariq 15:16–18, etc.	A piercing flame is a shooting star—a weapon of God used to strike devils.	Meteorites are solid lumps of matter which survive passage through the earth's atmosphere and reach the ground.

REFERENCE	STATEMENT	FACT
Noah 71:15–16 The Dominion 67:3 The Believers 23:17, 86, etc.	There are seven heavens, one above the other. Each holds different things—the lower being fitted with lights.	Groupings of stars do not match the layering description in any way.
The Prophets 21:31 The Bee 16:15 Luqman 31:10 The News 78:6–8 The Overwhelming 88:17, 19	God threw down mountains like tent pegs to keep the earth from shaking.	Mountains do not keep the earth from shaking and are not in any way like tent pegs.
The Women 4:23 (Al-Nisa) The Heights 7:172 (Al-Araf)	Semen comes from the back or kidney area, not from the testicles.	Semen comes from the testicles.
Resurrection 75:37–39 (Al-Qiyama) The Believer 40:67 (Al-Mumin) The Pilgrimage 22:5 (Al-Haij) The Believers 23:12–14 (Al-Muminun)	Humans are pro-duced by an ejacu-lated sperm that becomes (alaqa in Arabic) a leech-like clot, a clot of blood, a clot, depending upon which transla-tion you use.	Human development does not involve anything that fits the Koran's description.
The Women 4:23 (Al-Nisa)	Nursing passes on genetic traits from mother to child.	No genetic traits are transmitted by nursing.

REFERENCE	STATEMENT	FACT
The Ant 27:15–44 (Al-Naml)	Solomon talked with ants, birds, and giants (not presented as a miracle or a fable).	This kind of communication does not happen.

Source: *The Qur'an and the Bible in the Light of History and Science* by Dr. William Campbell, available from Reasons to Believe, PO Box 5978, Pasadena, CA 91117-0978, www.reasons.org.

Appendix B

APPENDIX B

This appendix contains four charts about accuracy in several different religions. The charts are:

Difficult Passages in the Koran
Hindu Beliefs
Basic Buddhism by Dalai Llama 6/01
Islam and Christianity Compared

Difficult Passages in the Koran

The following passages are taken from the *Koran*, translated by N. J. Dawood, Penguin Classics ©1974. Only a few passages from each subject area are given.

SUBJECT	QUOTE	LOCATION
Sky	He holds the sky from falling down.	Pilgrimage 22:65
Creation time	… created the earth in two days?	Revelations Well Expounded 41:9
Four or eight kinds of cattle	He has given you four different pairs of cattle.	Hordes 39:5
	He has given you eight kinds of livestock.	Cattle 6:143

SUBJECT	QUOTE	LOCATION
Life from water	We made every living thing of water?	Prophets 21:30
Man's creation	… Allah … has made you in gradual stages?	Noah 71:8–20
	Does man forget that we created him out of the void	Mary 19:67
	Did We not create you from an unworthy fluid, …	Those That Are Sent Forth 77:8–27
	… created you from dust, from a little germ, …	The Cave 18:35–39
	… unbelievers … Of coarse clay We created them.	Ranks 37:1–18
	He (Allah) who created man from water and gave him kindred of blood and of marriage.	Al-Furqan 25:53–55
	We first created man from an essence of clay: then placed him, a living germ, in a safe enclosure. The germ we made a clot of blood and the clot a lump of flesh. This we fashioned into bones, then clothed the bones with flesh, thus bringing forth another creation.	The Believers 23:1–16
	We created man from dry clay, from black moulded loam, …	Al-Hijr 15:21–31
Noah's sons	… Noah's son was drowned.	Houd 11:43

SUBJECT	QUOTE	LOCATION
Noah's sons	"Noah prayed to Us and his prayers were graciously answered. We delivered him and all his tribe … ."	The Ranks 37:70–80
Suicide	If any one thinks that Allah will not give victory to His apostle in this world and in the world to come, let him tie a rope to the ceiling of his house and hang himself.	Pilgrimage 22:11–16
Violence	Those who avenge themselves when wronged incur no guilt	Counsel 42:42–43
	When you meet the unbelievers in the battlefield strike off their heads … .	Mohammed 47:3–5
	… retaliation is decreed for you in bloodshed:	The Cow 2:178
	Fighting is obligatory for you,	The Cow 2:216
	As for the man or woman who is guilty of theft, cut off their hands punish them for their crimes.	The Table 5:37–39
Polygamy	… restrain their carnal desire save with their wives and slave girls … for these are lawful to them … .	The Ladders 70:22–29 The Believers 23:1–6

SUBJECT	QUOTE	LOCATION
Polygamy	… We have made lawful to you the wives to whom you have granted dowries and the slave girls whom Allah has given you as booty: the daughter of your paternal and maternal uncles and of your paternal and maternal aunts who fled with you; and the other women who gave themselves to you and whom you wish to take in marriage.	The Confederate Tribes 33:49–50
	If a man divorces his wife, he cannot remarry her until she has wedded another man and been divorced by him:	The Cow 2:230
	If you fear that you cannot treat orphans with fairness, then you may marry other women who seem good to you: two, three, or four of them.	Women 4:2–4
	You are also forbidden to take in marriage married women, except captives whom you own as slaves.	Women 4:24
Prostitution	You shall not force your slave-girls into prostitution … If they wish to preserve their chastity.	Light 24:33–34
Women	As for those whom you fear disobedience, admonish them and send them to beds apart and beat them.	Women 4:34

SUBJECT	QUOTE	LOCATION
Women	You may put off any of your wives you please and take to your bed any of them you please. Nor is it unlawful for you to receive any of those whom you have temporarily set aside … It shall be unlawful for you to take more wives or to change your present wives for other women, though their beauty please you except where slave-girls are concerned.	The Confeder-ate Tribes 33:51–52
Miscellan-eous	We changed them (men who were wrongdoers) into detested apes.	The Heights 7:164-166
	… transforming them into apes and swine.	The Table 5:57–61
	He alone has knowledge of what is hidden: … He sends down guardians who walk before them and behind them, that He may know if they have indeed delivered His messages.	The Jinn 72:25–28
Islam enemy of Christian-ity	The unbelievers among the People of the Book (Jews and Christians) and the pagans shall burn forever in the fire of Hell. They are the vilest of all creatures.	The Proof 98:6–7
	Those who say: 'The Lord of Mercy has begotten a son,' preach a monstrous falsehood ….	Mary 19:88

SUBJECT	QUOTE	LOCATION
Islam enemy of Christianity	Jesus was no more than a mortal whom we favored and made an example to the Israelites … .	Ornaments of Gold 43:1–11
	Make war on them (Christians and Jews) until idolatry is no more and Allah's religion reigns supreme.	The Spoils 8:37–41
	When the sacred months are over slay the idolaters (Christians and Jews) wherever you find them. Arrest them, besiege them, and lie in ambush everywhere for them.	Repentance 9:4–7
	Believers, make war on the infidels (Christian and Jews) who dwell around you.	Repentance 9:122–125
	Unbelievers are those who declare Allah is the Messiah, the Son of Mary.	The Table 5:17
	Believers, take neither Jews nor Christians for your friends … whosoever of you seeks their friendship shall become one of their number.	The Table 5:50–51
	Make war … .	Repentance 9:14

SUBJECT	QUOTE	LOCATION
Physical concept versus spiritual	This is the Paradise which the righteous have been promised. There shall flow in it rivers of unpolluted water, the rivers of milk forever fresh; rivers of delectable wine and rivers of clearest honey. They shall eat therein of every fruit and receive forgiveness from their Lord. Is this like the lot of those who shall abide in Hell forever and drink scalding water which will tear their bowels?	Mohammed 47:15
	As for the true servants of Allah, generous provisions shall be made for them: they shall feast on fruit and be honored in the gardens of delight. Reclining face to face upon soft couches, they shall be served with a goblet filled at a gushing fountain. Their drink shall neither dull their senses nor befuddle them. And by their side shall sit bashful, dark-eyed virgins as chaste as the sheltered eggs of ostriches. They will put questions to each other … .	The Ranks 37:40–56

Hindu Beliefs

The Hindu caste system as depicted by Gobi David, a dalit artist. From top: Brahmins; warriors and merchants; shudras and peasants; and untouchables

1. In a one, all-pervasive Supreme Being who is both immanent and transcendent, both Creator and Un-manifest Reality.
2. That the universe undergoes endless cycles of creation, preservation, and dissolution.
3. That all souls are evolving toward union with God and will ultimately find spiritual knowledge and liberation from the cycle of rebirth. Not a single soul will be eternally deprived of this destiny.
4. In karma, the law of cause and effect by which each individual creates his own destiny by his thoughts, words, and deeds.
5. That the soul reincarnates, evolving through many births until all karmas have been solved.
6. That divine beings exist in unseen inner worlds and that temple worship, rituals, and sacraments as well as personal devotionals create a communion with the devas and gods.
7. That a spiritually awakened Master is essential to know the Transcendent Absolute, as are personal discipline, good conduct, purification, self-inquiry, and meditation.
8. That all life is sacred and to be loved and revered, through the practice of non-violence.
9. That no particular religion teaches the only way to salvation above all others, but that all genuine religious paths are facets of God's Pure Love and Light, deserving tolerance and understanding.

Sources:

Natural History magazine

C. B. Subrahanyhim

Stan Guthrie, *Christianity Today*, February 8, 1993, page 48

Basic Buddhism by Dalai Llama 6/01

1. The current universe has evolved through natural law.
2. Truth has been given through the ages by various Buddhas or enlightened ones.
3. Gautama Buddha, who lived 2,500 years ago, is the teacher of our era.
4. While salvation depends on individual effort, the Buddhist is to take refuge in the Buddha, his teaching (dharma) and the Buddhist community (sangha).
5. The Buddha taught Four Noble Truths:
   a. Suffering is real;
   b. Suffering is caused by selfish desire;
   c. Suffering will cease when selfish desire is eliminated; and
   d. Selfish desire will cease through following the Noble Eightfold Path.
6. The Noble Eightfold Path that leads to nirvana involves:
   a. Right View
   b. Right Resolve
   c. Right Speech
   d. Right Action
   e. Right Livelihood
   f. Right Effort
   g. Right Mindfulness
   h. Right Concentration
7. All living things are subject to the law of karma, the principle of cause and effect, which controls the cycle of reincarnation.
8. The Buddhist is to abstain from killing, stealing, forbidden sex, lying, and the use of illicit drugs and liquor.
9. There is no God or Supreme Creator.
10. Buddhism is not irrational, pessimistic, or nihilistic.

By Jim Beverly, *Christianity Today*, June 11, 2001, page 66

Islam and Christianity Compared

by Lee Turner (a former missionary in Afghanistan) via *Pulpit Helps*, April 2001. The Bible references are from the New International Version.

"Any one who attacketh you, attack him in like manner as he attacked you" (Qur'an 2:194).	"But I tell you, Do not resist an evil person. If someone strikes you on the right cheek, turn to him the other also" (Matthew 5:39).
"… your almsgiving … will atone for some of your ill-deeds" (Qur'an 2:271).	"He saved us, not because of righteous things we had done, but because of His mercy. He saved us through the washing of rebirth and renewal by the Holy Spirit" (Titus 3:5).
"If ye avoid the great [things] which ye are forbidden, We will remit from you your evil deeds and make you enter at a noble gate" (Qur'an 4:31).	"For whoever keeps the whole law and yet stumbles at just one point is guilty of breaking all of it" (James 2:10).
"Seek ye to guide whom Allah hath sent astray? … if they turn back [to enmity] then take them and kill them wherever ye find them …" (Qur'an 4:88–89).	"Or do you show contempt for the riches of his kindness, tolerance and patience, not realizing that God's kindness leads you toward repentance?" (Romans 2:4).

"The Messiah, Jesus Son of Mary, was only a messenger of Allah, and His word which He conveyed to Mary, and spirit from Him. So believe Allah and His messengers, and say not Three' Cease [it is] better for you! Allah is only one God. Far is it removed from His transcendent majesty that He should have a son" (Qur'an 4:171).	"Come near me and listen to this: 'From the first announcement I have not spoken in secret; at the time it happens, I am there.' And now the Sovereign Lord has sent me, with his Spirit" (Isaiah 48:16). "For in Christ all the fullness of the Deity lives in bodily form, …" (Colossians 2:9).
"It is not for any prophet to have captives until he hath made slaughter in the land" (Qur'an 8:67).	"Bless those who persecute you; bless and do not curse. … Do not repay anyone evil for evil. Be careful to do what is right in the eyes of everybody. … Do not be overcome by evil, but overcome evil with good" (Romans 12:14, 17, 21).
"Freedom from obligation [is proclaimed] from Allah and His messenger toward those of the idolaters with whom ye made a treaty" (Qur'an 9:1).	"Again, you have heard that it was said to the people long ago, 'Do not break your oath, but keep the oaths you have made to the Lord'" (Matthew 5:33).

CALCULATED ODDS FOR BEING SUITABLY LOCATED IN OUR GALAXY

To calculate the probabilities of having a solar system located in one of the inhabitable doughnuts, we will compare the volume of the total galaxy with the volume of the doughnuts.

If we assume the galaxy to be 100,000 light-years (ly) in diameter and of an average thickness of four ly, we would have a cylinder whose volume could be calculated. Such a calculation would reveal the volume of the galaxy to be 3.14×10^{10} cubic ly.

Measurements of the magnetic field of our galaxy show that small changes from our solar system's position would produce radical magnetic changes fatal to our existence. A similar calculation shows gravitational variances to be even more critical.

If we approximate these estimates, we could hypothesize a "safe" doughnut size shown in figure Al.l. By subtracting a volume of the inner cylinder from the outer, we can establish a doughnut volume of approximately 1.04×10^8, which we double since there are two possible doughnuts. The ratio of 2.08×10^8 to the galaxy volume of 3.14×10^{10} gives us a probability of roughly 1 in 150 on being located at the proper place in the galaxy to have a solar system like our own.

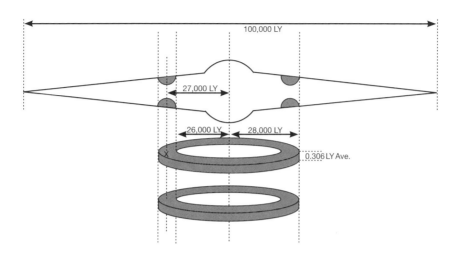

Figure A1.1: Approximate doughnut-shaped area in a spiral galaxy where a solar system could exist

MORE ON UNIVERSAL CONSTANTS

THE GRAVITATIONAL CONSTANT

Newton's universal law of gravity states that the force of gravity is proportional to the product of the masses divided by the square of the distance between the two masses. If we wanted to find out how much gravitational force there is between the earth and the moon, we could multiply the mass of the earth by the mass of the moon and divide by the distance from the earth to the moon squared.

In order for this to work, however, we have to include the gravitational constant. This is a proportionality constant that makes the equation work. I can say cents = dollars, but unless I put the proportionality constant into the equation, it is not a true statement. Cents = 100 (cents/dollar) times dollars is a true statement.

In the same way, Newton's universal law has a gravitational constant of 6.67×10^{-11}. This value for gravity works experimentally and in theory. It allows matter to exist and is vital to many areas of science. Einstein's improvements in defining gravity have not invalidated our understanding of its effects or changed the value of the gravitational constant.

THE ELECTRICAL CONSTANT

A similar type of discussion applies to electrical forces. In figure A2.1 we have the equation for electrical interaction between charged particles. Notice that the electrical equation is similar in form to the gravity equation with a constant that is huge compared to the gravitational constant. All electrical repulsive and attractive forces between charges are described by this equation.

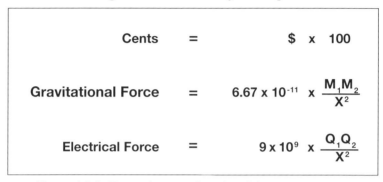

$$\text{Cents} = \$ \times 100$$

$$\text{Gravitational Force} = 6.67 \times 10^{-11} \times \frac{M_1 M_2}{X^2}$$

$$\text{Electrical Force} = 9 \times 10^{9} \times \frac{Q_1 Q_2}{X^2}$$

Figure A2.1: Example equations involving constants

The list in figure A2.2 gives some of the more commonly used constants. If it is supposed that the cosmos began by an explosion or inflation or any totally non intelligent chance process, how could all of these constants have arrived at the precise values that allow water and carbon and life to exist?

When a material changes state from liquid to a solid, a liquid to a gas, or a solid to a gas, additional energy is required to make the transition. This again is a design feature that is very important to our survival. If this extra energy, called the heat of fusion in the change from ice to water, were not required, all the ice in the world would immediately convert to water the instant the air temperature reached 33°F.

The flood produced by such an event would be cataclysmic. The physical reason this additional energy is needed involves the "locking" together of oppositely charged atoms in the freezing of the material.

In water, for example, the attractions between molecules in the solid state might look like the illustration in figure A2.3. The shaded areas show places where polar bonds are forming to lock the water molecules into a definite crystal lattice.

Constant	Value
Speed of Light in Vacuum	2.99792458×10^8 m/s
Gravitational Constant	$6.6726(5) \times 10^{-11}$ N·m²/kg²
Avogadro's Number	$6.022045(31) \times 10^{23}$ mol⁻¹
Gas Constant	$8.31441(26)$ J/mol·K
Boltzmann's Constant	$1.380662(44) \times 10^{-23}$ J/K
Stefan-Boltzmann Constant	$5.67032(71) \times 10^{-8}$ W/m²·K⁴
Permittivity of Free Space	8.99×10^9 kg·m³/s²·C²
Permeability of Free Space	$4\pi \times 10^{-7}$ T·m/A
Planck's Constant	$6.626176(36) \times 10^{-34}$ J·s

Figure A2.2: Necessary universal constants

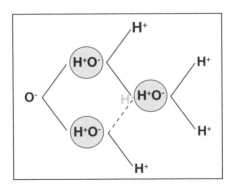

Figure A2.3: Example of polar bonds

STRING THEORY

Another subject discussed by Stephen Hawking in his book *A Brief History of Time* relates to what is called "string theory" (1988, 159–162). This subject is very complicated and can only be briefly highlighted here. String theory addresses the difference between Einstein's general theory of relativity and quantum mechanics, which are fundamentally incompatible. Quantum mechanics explains the relationship between particles closer together than the Planck length of 1 million billion billion billionth of a centimeter (10^{-33}), leaving general relativity to deal with the larger distances. For this reason, string theory has been called the "Theory of Everything" (TOE).

We mention string theory because at least eleven spacial dimensions are required to make it work. Being familiar with the four dimensions of height, length, width, and time, we may find it hard to imagine an additional seven. However, though extra dimensions cannot be visualized, they are readily described mathematically and are believed to exist physically. If, in fact, it does take an extra seven dimensions to explain the existence of the universe, where are they today? Since these seven dimensions are needed only to unify the four fundamental forces at distances less than 10^{-33} centimeters, it is believed that they stopped growing at this level of expansion during the big bang.

Today, strings are accepted as being, in one way or another, the elementary particle-like components of all matter, having various shapes like one- or two-dimensional filaments that vibrate within all dimensions of superspace at the same time. It is the different modes of vibration that give strings their identifying properties (Green 1999, 142–146).

These facts, if true, have profound implications. While we are personally limited to experiencing only four dimensions of space, all matter has higher dimensional components at the smallest scale of existence. Since God has the ability to access these extra dimensions, quantum mechanics and string theory give us a physical explanation for how God can control everything, including time itself.

Appendix 4

HOW MANY STARS ARE THERE?

If we assume that the universe began with a big bang, then that explosion-like event took place at a particular point in time and space. If it took place 20 billion years ago (a much older figure than many astronomers believe), nothing in the cosmos could be older than that figure. The light from that explosion would have traveled to a point 20 billion light-years from the point of the explosion. (See figure A4.1, next page.) If you could go out to point G in the figure, you could, in theory, see the big bang take place.

Let us now do some crude calculations to find out how many galaxies there are in space potentially available to us. If we assume that the big bang was a uniform explosion creating a uniform space, the cosmos would be a sphere. The volume of that sphere could be calculated by the formula $V=4/3\pi r^3$ from elementary math. That would be $4/3(\pi)(20\text{ billion})^3$ which works out to be approximately 10^{30} cubic light-years.

In appendix 1 (page 183), we calculated the volume of our galaxy to be 3.14×10^{10} cubic light-years. Notice that if there were no space at all between galaxies (and there is), the number of possible galaxies in space would be 10^{30} divided by 3.14×10^{10}, or roughly 10^{20} galaxies. If each of these galaxies contained 100 billion stars (and most contain fewer), the total number of stars would be $10^{20} \times 10^{11}$ or roughly 10^{31}. The odds we have been describing are on

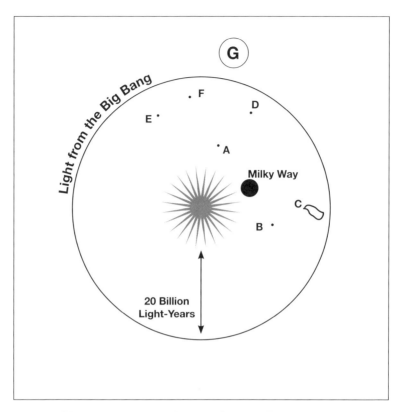

Figure A4.1: The "Big Bang" view of the cosmos

the order of 1 in 10^{160}. For more complex proteins, these odds can quickly reduce to 1 in 10^{1000} (see page 43ff). Based on either of these numbers, there are not nearly enough stars in the cosmos to allow chance to be a working factor in explaining the design we see.

THE VARIABLE NATURE OF TIME

$$T = \frac{T_0}{\sqrt{1-(V^2/c^2)}}$$

In the equation, T_0 represents the time a person would experience if he or she were in a totally static condition, not moving through space at all. You may not realize it, but at this moment, you are traveling through space at about 600,000 miles per hour, because that is the speed of the earth through space. T then represents the time that we actually do experience and how long it is compared to static time. V is the speed the person or object is moving, and c is the speed of light in a vacuum, approximately 186,317 miles per second.

This equation, then, suggests that time is variable. Upon examining the equation, it becomes clear that, as one goes faster and faster (as V increases), the value of T becomes larger and larger (time slows down). As V approaches c in magnitude, V^2/c^2 gets close to 1, and the denominator approaches zero, which makes the value of T become nearly infinite. In other words, each static second could become infinitely long by comparison. Now you know what happens when "time flies."

EVIDENCE FOR DESIGN
IN THE UNIVERSE

1. Gravitational coupling constant	If larger:	No stars less than 1.4 solar masses, hence short stellar life spans
	If smaller:	No stars more than 0.8 solar masses, hence no heavy element production
2. Strong nuclear force coupling constant	If larger:	No hydrogen; nuclei essential for life are unstable
	If smaller:	No elements other than hydrogen
3. Weak nuclear force coupling constant	If larger:	All hydrogen is converted to helium in the big bang, hence too much heavy elements
	If smaller:	No helium produced from big bang, hence not enough heavy elements
4. Electromagnetic coupling constant	If larger:	No chemical bonding; elements more massive than boron are unstable to fission
	If smaller:	No chemical bonding

from a paper "Limits for the Universe" by Hugh Ross, Ph.D., updated to "Astronomical Evidences for the God of the Bible," which is available online at http://www.reasons.org

5. Ratio of protons to electrons formation	If larger:	Electromagnetism dominates gravity preventing galaxy, star, and planet formation
	If smaller:	Electromagnetism dominates gravity preventing galaxy, star, and planet formation
6. Ratio of electron to proton mass	If larger:	No chemical bonding
	If smaller:	No chemical bonding
7. Expansion rate of the universe	If larger:	No galaxy formation
	If smaller:	Universe collapses prior to star formation
8. Entropy level of universe	If larger:	No star condensation within the proto-galaxies
	If smaller:	No proto-galaxy formation
9. Mass density of the universe	If larger:	Too much deuterium from big bang, hence stars burn too rapidly
	If smaller:	No helium from big bang, hence not enough heavy elements
10. Age of the universe	If older:	No solar-type stars in a stable burning phase in the right part of the galaxy
	If younger:	Solar-type stars in a stable burning phase would not yet have formed
11. Initial uniformity of radiation	If smoother:	Stars, star clusters, and galaxies would not have formed
	If coarser:	Universe by now would be mostly black holes and empty space
12. Average distance between stars	If larger:	Heavy element density too thin for rocky planet production
	If smaller:	Planetary orbits become destabilized
13. Solar luminos-ity	If increases too soon:	Runaway green house effect
	If increases too late:	Frozen oceans
14. Fine structure constant*	If larger:	No stars more than 0.7 solar masses
	If smaller:	No stars less then 1.8 solar masses

*(A function of three other fundamental constants, Planck's constant, the velocity of light, and the electron charge each of which, therefore, must be fine-tuned)

15. Decay rate of the proton	If greater:	Life would be exterminated by the release of radiation
	If smaller:	Insufficient matter in the universe for life
16. ^{12}C to ^{16}O energy level ratio	If larger:	Insufficient oxygen
	If smaller:	Insufficient carbon
17. Decay rate of ^8Be	If slower:	Heavy element fusion would generate catastrophic explosions in all the stars
	If faster:	No element production beyond beryllium and, hence, no life chemistry possible
18. Mass difference between the neutron and the proton	If greater:	Protons would decay before stable nuclei could form
	If smaller:	Protons would decay before stable nuclei could form
19. Initial excess of nucleons over anti-nucleons	If greater:	Too much radiation for planets to form
	If smaller:	Not enough matter for galaxies or stars to form
20. Galaxy type	If too elliptical:	Star formation ceases before sufficient heavy element buildup for life chemistry
	If too irregular:	Radiation exposure on occasion is too severe and/or heavy elements for life chemistry are not available
21. Parent star distance from center of galaxy	If farther:	Quantity of heavy elements would be insufficient to make rocky planets
	If closer:	Stellar density and radiation would be too great
22. Number of stars in the planetary system	If more than one:	Tidal interactions would disrupt planetary orbits
	If less than one:	Heat produced would be insufficient for life
23. Parent star birth date	If more recent:	Star would not yet have reached stable burning phase
	If less recent:	Stellar system would not yet contain enough heavy elements

24. Parent star age	If older:	Luminosity of star would change too quickly
	If younger:	Luminosity of star would change too quickly
25. Parent star mass	If greater:	Luminosity of star would change too quickly; star would burn too rapidly
	If less:	Range of distances appropriate for life would be too narrow; tidal forces would disrupt the rotational period for a planet of the right distance; uv radiation would be inadequate for plants to make sugars and oxygen
26. Parent star color	If redder:	Photosynthetic response would be insufficient
	If bluer:	Photosynthetic response would be insufficient
27. Supernovae eruptions	If too close:	Life on the planet would be exterminated
	If too far:	Not enough heavy element ashes for the formation of rocky planets
	If too infrequent:	Not enough heavy element ashes for the formation of rocky planets
	If too frequent:	Life on the planet would be exterminated
28. White dwarf binaries	If too few:	Insufficient fluorine produced for life chemistry to proceed
	If too many:	Disruption of planetary orbits from stellar density; life on the planet would be exterminated
29. Surface gravity (escape velocity)	If stronger:	Atmosphere would retain too much ammonia and methane
	If weaker:	Planet's atmosphere would lose too much water
30. Distance from parent star	If farther:	Planet would be too cool for a stable water cycle
	If closer:	Planet would be too warm for a stable water cycle

31. Inclination of orbit	If too great: Temperature differences on the planet would be too extreme
32. Orbital eccentricity	If too great: Seasonal temperature differences would be too extreme
33. Axial tilt	If greater: Surface temperature differences would be too great If less: Surface temperature differences would be too great
34. Rotation period	If longer: Diurnal temperature differences would be too great If shorter: Atmospheric wind velocities would be too great
35. Gravitational interaction with a moon	If greater: Tidal effects on the oceans, atmosphere, and rotational period would be too severe If less: Orbital obliquity changes would cause climatic instabilities
36. Magnetic field	If stronger: Electromagnetic storms would be too severe If weaker: Inadequate protection from hard stellar radiation
37. Thickness of crust	If thicker: Too much oxygen would be transferred from the atmosphere to the crust If thinner: Volcanic and tectonic activity would be too great
38. Albedo (ratio of reflected light to total amount falling on surface)	If greater: Runaway ice age would develop If less: Runaway greenhouse effect would develop
39. Oxygen to nitrogen ratio in atmosphere	If larger: Advanced life functions would proceed too quickly If smaller: Advanced life functions would proceed too slowly

40. Carbon dioxide level in atmosphere	If greater:	Runaway greenhouse effect would develop
	If less:	Plants would not be able to maintain efficient photosynthesis
41. Water vapor level in atmosphere	If greater:	Runaway greenhouse effect would develop
	If less:	Rainfall would be too meager for advanced life on the land
42. Ozone level in atmosphere	If greater:	Surface temperatures would be too low
	If less:	Surface temperatures would be too high; there would be too much uv radiation at the surface
43. Atmospheric electric discharge rate	If greater:	Too much fire destruction would occur
	If less:	Too little nitrogen would be fixed in the atmosphere
44. Oxygen quantity in atmosphere	If greater:	Plants and hydrocarbons would burn up too easily
	If less:	Advanced animals would have too little to breathe
45. Oceans to continents ratio	If greater:	Diversity and complexity of life-forms would be limited
	If smaller:	Diversity and complexity of life-forms would be limited
46. Soil material-izations	If too nutrient poor: Diversity and complexity of life-forms would be limited
	If too nutrient rich: Diversity and complexity of life-forms would be limited
47. Seismic activity	If greater:	Too many life-forms would be destroyed
	If less:	Nutrients on ocean floors (from river runoff) would not be recycled to the continents through tectonic uplift

Appendix 7

HEBREW WORDS AND DEFINITIONS IN GENESIS 1:1–31; 2:1–3

Understanding the Hebrew definitions of some of the key words in the Genesis creation account is helpful to our discussion. Following is the biblical account with key Hebrew words placed above the text. The English word or words to which each Hebrew word corresponds are underlined. Following the biblical text is an alphabetical list of the Hebrew words and their definitions. Then in Appendix 8 (page 211), there is a list of the animals mentioned in the biblical account, their Hebrew name and definition, and the verses in which they are mentioned. (Words supplied by the translators of the King James Version are in italics.)

            reshith elohim bara   shamayim   erets
1:1) In the <u>beginning</u> <u>God</u> <u>created</u> the <u>heaven</u> and the <u>earth</u>.

       erets   *tohu*   *bohu*   *choshek*
2) And the <u>earth</u> was without <u>form</u>, and <u>void</u>; and <u>darkness</u>

            panim   *tehom*   *ruach*
was upon the <u>face</u> of the <u>deep</u>. And the <u>Spirit of God</u>

 rachaph   *panim*   *mayim*   *elohim*
<u>moved</u> upon the <u>face</u> of the <u>waters</u>. 3) And <u>God</u> said, Let

       or   *or*   *elohim*
there be <u>light</u>: and there was <u>light</u>. 4) And <u>God</u> saw the

The Source • 201

    or   *tob*   *elohim badal*   *or*

light, that it *was* good: and God divided the light from the

   choshek   *elohim*   *or* *yom*   *choshek*

darkness. 5) And God called the light Day, and the darkness

               layelah,
               layil   *ereb*   *boqer*

he called Night. And the evening and the morning were the

   echad yom   *elohim*   *raqia*

first day. 6) And God said, Let there be a firmament in the

 tavek   *mayim*   *badal*   *mayim*

midst of the waters, and let it divide the waters from the

 mayim   *elohim asah*   *raqia*   *badal*

waters. 7) And God made the firmament, and divided the

 mayim   *tachath*   *raqia*   *mayim*

waters which *were* under the firmament from the waters

                   raqia

which *were* above the firmament: and it was so. 8) And

elohim   *raqia*   *shamayim*   *ereb*

God called the firmament Heaven. And the evening and the

 boqer   *sheni* *yom*   *elohim*

morning were the second day. 9) And God said, Let the

mayim tachath   *shamayim*   *qavah*   *maqom*

waters under the heaven be gathered together unto one place,

     yabbashah raah   *elohim*

and let the dry *land* appear: and it was so. 10) And God

     yabbashah erets   *miqveh*

called the dry *land* Earth; and the gathering together of the

mayim   *yam*   *elohim*   *tob*

waters called he Seas: and God saw that it *was* good.

     elohim   *erets* *dasha* *deshe* *eseb*

11) And God said, Let the earth bring forth grass, the herb

zera   *ets*   *peri*   *min*

yielding <u>seed</u>, *and* the <u>fruit tree</u> yielding <u>fruit</u> after his <u>kind</u>,

zera   *erets*

whose <u>seed</u> *is* in itself, upon the <u>earth</u>: and it was so.

erets   *deshe*   *eseb*

12) And the <u>earth</u> brought forth <u>grass</u>, *and* <u>herb</u> yielding

zera   *min*   *ets*   *peri*   *zera*

<u>seed</u> after his <u>kind</u>, and the <u>tree</u> yielding <u>fruit</u>, whose <u>seed</u>

min   *elohim*   *tob*

was in itself, after his <u>kind</u>: and <u>God</u> saw that it *was* <u>good</u>.

ereb   *boqer*   *shelishi yom*

13) And the <u>evening</u> and the <u>morning</u> were the <u>third</u> <u>day</u>.

elohim   *maor*   *raqia*

14) And <u>God</u> said, Let there be <u>lights</u> in the <u>firmament</u> of

shamayim   *badal*   *yom*   *layelah, layil*

the <u>heaven</u> to <u>divide</u> the <u>day</u> from the <u>night</u>; and let them

oth   *moed*   *yom*   *shanah*

be for <u>signs</u>, and for <u>seasons</u>, and for <u>days</u>, and <u>years</u>:

maor   *raqia*

15) And let them be for <u>lights</u> in the <u>firmament</u> of the

shamayim   *or*   *erets*

<u>heaven</u> to give <u>light</u> upon the <u>earth</u>: and it was so.

elohim asah   *gadol maor*   *gadol maor*

16) And <u>God</u> <u>made</u> two <u>great</u> <u>lights</u>; the <u>greater</u> <u>light</u> to

memsheleth   *memsheleth*   *layelah*

yom   *gaton maor*   *layil*   *asah*

<u>rule</u> the <u>day</u>, and the <u>lesser</u> <u>light</u> to <u>rule</u> the <u>night</u>: *he* <u>*made*</u>

kakab   *elohim nathan*   *raqia*

the <u>stars</u> also. 17) And <u>God</u> <u>set</u> them in the <u>firmament</u> of

shamayim   *or*   *erets*   *mashal*

the <u>heaven</u> to give <u>light</u> upon the <u>earth</u>, 18) And to <u>rule</u>

                                         layelah,
         yom   *layil*   *badal*   *or*
over the <u>day</u> and over the <u>night</u>, and to <u>divide</u> the <u>light</u> from

         choshek   *elohim*   *tob*
the <u>darkness</u>: and <u>God</u> saw that *it was* <u>good</u>. 19) And the

       ereb   *boqer*   *rebii yom*   *elohim*
<u>evening</u> and the <u>morning</u> were the <u>fourth</u> <u>day</u>. 20) And <u>God</u>

                  mayim   *sharats*
said, Let the <u>waters</u> <u>bring forth</u> abundantly the

         sherets   *nephesh*   *oph*   *uph*
<u>moving creature</u> that hath <u>life</u>, and <u>fowl</u> *that* may <u>fly</u> above

         erets   *raqia*   *shamayim*   *elohim*
the <u>earth</u> in the open <u>firmament</u> of <u>heaven</u>. 21) And <u>God</u>

   bara   *tannin*   *chai*   *nephesh*
<u>created</u> great <u>whales</u>, and every <u>living</u> <u>creature that moveth</u>,

              mayim   *sharats*   *min*
which the <u>waters</u> <u>brought forth abundantly</u>, after their <u>kind</u>,

              kanaph oph   *min*   *elohim*
and every <u>winged</u> <u>fowl</u> after his <u>kind</u>: and <u>God</u> saw that *it*

           tob   *elohim barak*   *parah*
was <u>good</u>. 22) And <u>God</u> <u>blessed</u> them, saying, Be <u>fruitful</u>,

        rabah   *male*   *mayim*   *yam*   *oph*
and <u>multiply</u>, and <u>fill</u> the <u>waters</u> in the <u>seas</u>, and let <u>fowl</u>

   rabah   *erets*   *ereb*   *boqer*
<u>multiply</u> in the <u>earth</u>. 23) And the <u>evening</u> and the <u>morning</u>

        chamishshi,
        chamishi yom   *elohim*   *erets*
were the <u>fifth</u> <u>day</u>. 24) And <u>God</u> said, Let the <u>earth</u>

       sharats   *nephesh*   *min behemah*
<u>bring forth</u> the <u>living creature</u> after his <u>kind</u>, <u>cattle</u>, and

       remes   *chaiyah, cheva*   *min*
<u>creeping thing</u>, and <u>beast of the earth</u> after his <u>kind</u>: and it

        elohim *asah*   *chaiyah, cheva*

was so. 25) And <u>God</u> <u>made</u> the <u>beast of the earth</u> after his

min   *behemah*   *min*   *remes*

<u>kind</u>, and <u>cattle</u> after their <u>kind</u>, and every <u>thing that creepeth</u>

        erets   *min*   *elohim*

upon the <u>earth</u> after his <u>kind</u>: and <u>God</u> saw that *it was*

 tob   *elohim*   *asah adam*   *tselem*

<u>good</u>. 26) And <u>God</u> said, Let us <u>make</u> <u>man</u> in our <u>image</u>,

       demuth   *radah*   *dagah*

after our <u>likeness</u>: and let them have <u>dominion</u> over the <u>fish</u>

     yam   *oph*   *behemah*

of the <u>sea</u>, and over the <u>fowl</u> of the air, and over the <u>cattle</u>,

        erets   *remes*

and over all the <u>earth</u>, and over every <u>creeping thing</u> that

 remes   *erets*   *elohim bara adam*

<u>creepeth</u> upon the <u>earth</u>. 27) So <u>God</u> <u>created</u> <u>man</u> in his

    tselem   *tselem elohim bara*   *zakar*

own <u>image</u>, in the <u>image</u> of <u>God</u> <u>created</u> he him; <u>male</u> and

neqebah bara   *elohim barak*

<u>female</u> <u>created</u> he them. 28) And <u>God</u> <u>blessed</u> them, and

elohim   *parah*   *rabah*   *male*

<u>God</u> said unto them, Be <u>fruitful</u>, and <u>multiply</u>, and <u>replenish</u>

   erets   *kabash*   *radah*   *dagah*

the <u>earth</u>, and <u>subdue</u> it: and have <u>dominion</u> over the <u>fish</u> of

    yam   *oph*

the <u>sea</u>, and over the <u>fowl</u> of the air, and over every

     chaiyah   *erets*   *elohim*

<u>living thing that moveth</u> upon the <u>earth</u>. 29) And <u>God</u> said,

hinneh   *eseb*   *zera*

<u>Behold</u>, I have given you every <u>herb</u> bearing <u>seed</u>, which *is*

panim   *erets*   *ets*

upon the <u>face</u> of all the <u>earth</u>, and every <u>tree</u>, in the which

peri   *ets*   *zera*

is the <u>fruit</u> of a <u>tree</u> yielding <u>seed</u>; to you it shall be for

oklah   *chaiyah, cheva*   *erets*

<u>meat</u>. 30) And to every <u>beast</u> of the <u>earth</u>, and to every

oph   *remes*

<u>fowl</u> of the air, and to every thing that <u>creepeth upon</u> the

erets   *nephesh*   *yereq eseb*

<u>earth</u>, wherein *there is* <u>life</u>, *I have given* every <u>green</u> <u>herb</u>

oklah   *elohim*

for <u>meat</u>: and it was so. 31) And <u>God</u> saw every thing that

asah   *meod tob*

he had <u>made</u>, and, behold, *it was* <u>very</u> <u>good</u>. And the

ereb   *boqer*   *shishshi yom*

<u>evening</u> and the <u>morning</u> were the <u>sixth</u> <u>day</u>. 2:1) Thus the

shamayim   *erets*   *kalah*   *tsaba*

<u>heavens</u> and the <u>earth</u> were <u>finished</u>, and all the <u>host</u> of

shebii   *yom elohim kalah*   *melakah*

them. 2) And on the <u>seventh</u> <u>day</u> <u>God</u> <u>ended</u> his <u>work</u>

asah   *shabath*   *shebii*   *yom*

which he had <u>made</u>; and he <u>rested</u> on the <u>seventh</u> <u>day</u> from

melakah   *asah*   *elohim barak*

all his <u>work</u> which he had <u>made</u>. 3) And <u>God</u> <u>blessed</u> the

shebii   *yom*   *qadesh*

<u>seventh</u> <u>day</u>, and <u>sanctified</u> it: because that in it he had

shabath   *melakah*   *elohim bara*   *asah*

<u>rested</u> from all his <u>work</u> which <u>God</u> <u>created</u> and <u>made</u>.

WORDS AND DEFINITIONS

Hebrew word	Hebrew Definition
asah	to do, make (applies to man or God—reworking existing material)
adam	a man, human being
badal	to separate
bara	to prepare, form, fashion, create (applies only to God. Fiat creation—a miracle)
barak	to declare blessed
behemah	cattle, beast
bohu	emptiness
boqer	morning
chai	living, alive, lively
chaiyah	living being
chaiyah, cheva	a living creature
chamishshi, chamishi	fifth
choshek	darkness
dagah	fish
dasha	to cause to yield tender grass
demuth	likeness
deshe	tender grass (lichen, algae, etc.)
echad	one, first
elohim	God, (plural—implies power of God)
ereb	evening
erets	earth, land (refers to functional planet—648 uses in O. T.)
eseb	herb (naked seed—fern—gymnosperm)
ets	a tree, wood, timber, stick
gadol	great

Hebrew word	Hebrew Definition
hinneh	see
kabash	to subdue
kakab	a star
kalah	to be completed, finished
kanaph	a wing (as covering and protecting)
layelah, layil	night
male (Eng. fill)	to fill, complete (not to refill)
male (Eng. replenish)	to fill, be full
maor	light giver (or light holder)
mashal	to rule
maqom	a place of standing (or bowl)
mayim	waters, water
melakah	work
memsheleth	rule, dominion
meod	might, very
min	kind (broad term not equal to the scientific word species. See 1 Corinthians 15:39—same idea in Greek is brought out as kind)
miqveh	collection
moed	an appointed time or season
nathan	to give
nephesh (Eng. life)	living (or life) breath
nephesh (Eng. creature)	breathing creature
neqebah	a female
oklah	what is eaten, food
oph	fowl
or	light (Genesis 1:3, 4, 4, 5, 18) (See *maor* not used here)

Hebrew word	Hebrew Definition
or	to cause or give light (Genesis 1:15, 17)
oth	a sign
panim	face
parah	to be fruitful
peri	fruit (angiosperm, see zera)
qadesh	to separate, set apart
qaton	little, small, young
qavah	to be gathered, bound together
raah	to be seen
rabah	to be many, abundant
rachaph	to move, shake
radah	to rule (be responsible for)
raqia	expanse (interface — zone of change)
rebii	fourth
remes	a creeping creature, close to the earth (sheep, goats, smaller mammals — Jews could eat them)
reshith	first, former (absolute beginning point)
ruach	Spirit, wind
shabath	to cease, rest, keep sabbath
shamayim	heavens (heaved up things referring to space)
shanah	a year, repetition (identifiable cycles)
sharats	to swarm
shebii	seventh
shelishi	third
sheni	second, other, again
sherets	a teeming thing (implies a group of animals — all kinds)

Hebrew word	Hebrew Definition
shishshi	sixth
tachath	under, beneath
tannin	a great sea monster (implies any great sea creature)
tavek	middle, midst
tehom	deep place, the deep (sea)
tob	good
tohu	a ruin, vacancy (implies there was some thing to vacate)
tsaba	host, warfare, service
tselem	image (likeness of some kind)
uph	to fly
yabbashah	a dry place (as opposed to land that was not dry—swampy, under water)
yam	sea, lake, pool
yereq	green herb, greenness
yom	day (or time, forever, etc. See Deuteronomy 10:10)
zakar	male
zera	seed, seed time, progeny (true seed plant—angiosperm)

ANIMALS AND SEQUENCE OF GENESIS

ANIMALS OF GENESIS

English Name	Verses	Hebrew Name	Literal Meaning	Other Uses
moving creature	20	*sherets*	swarming creature	0
fowl	20, 21, 22, 26	*oph*	fowl	61
winged	21	*kanaph*	winged	78
whale	21	*tannin*	sea monster (Job 7:12; Ezekiel 32:2)	3
creature that moveth	21, 24	*nephesh*	breathing creature	8
cattle	24, 25, 36	*behemah*	cattle, beast	51
creeping thing	24, 25, 26	*remes*	creeping creature (Genesis 9:3)	16
beast	24, 25, 30	*chaiyah, cheva*	a living creature	114

English Name	Verses	Hebrew Name	Literal Meaning	Other Uses
fish	26, 28	*dagah*	fsh	33
behemoth	Job 40:15	*behemoth*	enlarged form behemah	0
leviathan	Job 41:1	*livyathan*	great water animal (Psalm 104:26)	3

THE SEQUENCE OF GENESIS

Bible Verse	Bible	Scientific Evidence
1	Creation	Big bang evidence
9–10	Water/one land	Continental drift
11–12	Grass/herb, etc.	First life—plants
20a & 21a	Sea creatures	First animals—marine
20b & 21b	Fowl	Birds—first warm blooded
24–25	Mammals	Mammals after birds
26–27	Man	Man is most recent

BIBLIOGRAPHIC RESOURCES

as of March 2010

Some of these books and references may be out of print—you will
have to check with your local or online bookseller. Books on this
list are avaible through your local or online bookseller. **Does God
Exist?** has only the books mentioned as being available through
Does God Exist?

Apologetics, General

Apologetics Materials. American Scientific Affiliation, PO Box J,
Ipswich, MA 01938.

Boa, Kenneth, and Robert Bowman. *20 Compelling Evidences
that God Exists*. Tulsa, Okla.: River Oak Publishing, 2002.

Craig, William. *Reasonable Faith*. Wheaton, Ill.: Crossway
Books, 2008.

Geisler, Norman L., and Frank Turek. *I Don't Have Enough Faith
to be an Atheist*. Wheaton, Ill.: Crossway Books, 2004.

Geisler, Norman L., and Thomas Howe. *When Critics Ask*. Grand
Rapids, Mich.: Baker Books, 2004.

Glynn, Patrick. *God: the Evidence*. Prima Publishing, 1997.

Heeren, Fred. *Show Me God*. Wheeling, Ill.: Searchlight
Publications, 1995.

Jacoby, Doug. *Genesis, Science and History*. Woburn, Mass.:
Discipleship Publications International, 2004.

McDowell, Josh. *The New Evidence that Demands a Verdict*.
Nashville, Tenn.: Thomas Nelson Publications, 1999.

Oakes, John. *Is There a God?* Long Beach, Calif.: Great
    Commission Illustrated, 1999.
Ross, Hugh, Reasons to Believe, PO Box 2289, Glendora, CA
    91740-2269.
Samples, Kenneth. *Without a Doubt.* Grand Rapids, Mich.: Baker
    Books, 2004.
Schaefer, Henry F. *Science and Christianity: Conflict
    or Coherence.* Watkinsville, Ga.: The Apollos Trust
    Publisher,2004.
Strobel, Lee. *The Case for Faith.* Grand Rapids, Mich.:
    Zondervan Publishing House, 2000.

Atheism

Boyd, Gregory A., and Edward K. *Letters from a Skeptic.* Cook
    Communications Ministries Publisher, 2004.
Evans, Craig. *Fabricating Jesus.* InterVarsity Press, Downers
    Grove, IL, 2006.
Harmon, O. E. *The Story of Liberal Missouri.* Liberal News, 1925,
    reprinted 1995 by Liberal Area Civic Group.
Humanist Manifestos I & II. Buffalo, N. Y.: Prometheus Books,
    2004.
Jones, Timothy Paul. *Misquoting Truth.* Downers Grove, Ill.:
    InterVarsity Press, 2007.
Koster, John P. *The Atheist Syndrome.* Brentwood, Tenn.: Wolgemuth
    & Hyatt Publishers, Inc., 1989.
McGrath, Alister. *The Twilight of Atheism.* Doubleday, 2004.
McGrath, Alister, and Joanna Collicutt McGrath. *The Dawkins
    Delusion.* Downers Grove, Ill.: InterVarsity Press. 2007.
Moore, J. P. *This Strange Town: Liberal, Missouri.* Dallas, Tex.:
    Liberal, Mo.: The Liberal News, 1963.
Vitz, Paul C. *Faith of the Fatherless.* Spence Publishing Co., 1999.
Zacharias, Ravi. *A Shattered Visage: The Real Face of Atheism.*
    Grand Rapids, Mich.: Baker Books, 1993.

Biblical Inspiration and World Religions

Behind the Veil. American Christian Family Association, PO Box
    12455, Burke, VA 22009.
Bock, Darrell. *Can I Trust the Bible?* Norcross, Ga.: Ravi
    Zacharias International Ministries, 2001.
Bollet, Alfred J. *Medical History in the Bible.* (Reprinted series of
    articles from Medical Times), 1986.

Bruce, F. F. *Jesus and Christian Origins Outside the New Testament*. Grand Rapids, Mich,: Wm. B. Eerdmans Publishing Co., 1974.

Bruce, F. F. *Canon of Scriptures*. Downers Grove, Ill.: InterVarsity Press, 1988.

Campbell, William. *The Quran and the Bible: In the Light of History and Science*. Middle East Resources, 1994.

Copan, Paul. *That's Just Your Interpretation*. Grand Rapids, Mich.: Baker Books, 2001

Dawood, N. J., translator. *The Koran*. New York, N.Y.: Viking Penguin Inc., 1974.

Fudge, Edward William. *The Fire That Consumes*. Houston, Tex.: Providential Press, 1982.

Fudge, Edward William, and Robert A. Peterson. *Two Views of Hell*. Downers Grove, Ill.: InterVarsity Press, 2000.

Geisler, Norman L., and Paul K. Hoffman. *Why I Am a Christian*. Grand Rapids, Mich.: Baker Book House, 2001.

Geisler, Norman L., and Thomas Howe. *When Critics Ask*. Grand Rapids, Mich.: Baker Books, 2004.

Habermas, Gary R. *The Historical Jesus*. Joplin, Mo.: College Press, 1996.

Jones, Timothy Paul. *Misquoting Truth*. Downers Grove, Ill.: InterVarsity Press, 2007.

Leeper, Wayne D. *Prelude to Glory*. Available from **Does God Exist?** 1555 Echo Valley Dr., Niles, MI 49120, 1987.

Lightfoot, Neil R. *How We Got the Bible*. Grand Rapids, Mich.: Baker Books, 2004.

McMillen, S. I. *None of These Diseases*. New York, N.Y.: Pyramid Publications, Inc., 1967.

Oakes, John M. *Reasons for Belief*. Spring, Tex.: Illumination Press International, 2005.

Orr-Ewing, Amy. *Is the Bible Intolerant?* Downers Grove, Ill.: InterVarsity Press, 2005.

Rogers, Oliver. *The Faith of Christ*. Mustang, Okla.: Tate Publishing, 2009.

Schmidt, Alvin J. *Under the Influence*. Grand Rapids, Mich.: Zondervan Publishing House, 2001.

Strobel, Lee. *The Case for Christ*. Grand Rapids, Mich.: Zondervan Publishing House, 1998.

Vaughan, Curtis, editor. *The Word: The Bible from 26 Translations*. Gulfport, Miss.: Mathis Publishers, 1993.

Williams, Stephen. *The Real Jesus of History*. Available from **Does God Exist?** 1555 Echo Valley Dr., Niles, MI 49120.

Wohlberg, Steve. *End Time Delusions*. Shippensburg, Penn.: Destiny Image Pub., 2004.

Zacharias, Ravi. *Jesus Among Other Gods*. Nashville, Tenn.: Word Publishing (a Thomas Nelson Company), 2000.

Zacharias, Ravi. *Light in the Shadow of Jihad*. Sisters, Oreg.: Multnomah Publishers Inc., 2002.

Zacharias, Ravi. *The Lotus and the Cross*. Sisters, Oreg.: Multnomah Publishers Inc., 2001.

Cosmology

Abbott, Edwin A. *Flatland*. New York, N.Y.: Dover Publications, Inc., 1952.

Craig, William Lane. *Time and Eternity*. Wheaton, Ill.: Crossway Books, 2001.

Ferguson, Kitty. *The Fire in the Equations*. Philadelphia, Pa.: Tempeton Foundation Press, 1994.

Hawking, Stephen. *A Brief History of Time*. New York, N.Y.: Bantam Books, 1988.

Hawking, Stephen. *The Universe in a Nutshell*. New York, N.Y.: Bantam Books, 2001.

Morrison, Phillip & Phylis. *Powers of Ten*. New York, N.Y.: Scientific American, 1982.

Peacock, Roy E. *A Brief History of Eternity*. Wheaton, Ill.: Crossway Books, 1990.

Ross, Hugh. *Beyond the Cosmos*. Colorado Springs, Colo.: NavPress, 1996.

Ross, Hugh. *Creation and Time*. Colorado Springs, Colo.: NavPress, 1994.

Ross, Hugh. *Creator and the Cosmos*. Colorado Springs, Colo.: NavPress, 1994.

Ross, Hugh. *The Fingerprint of God*. Pasadena, Calif.: Reasons to Believe, 1989.

Schroeder, Gerald L. *Genesis and the Big Bang*. New York, N.Y.: Bantam Books, 1990.

Stewart, Ian. *Flatterland*. Cambridge, Mass.: Perseus Publishing, 2001.

Design

Agosta, William. *Bombardier Beetles and Feeder Trees*. Addison-Wesley Co., 1996.

Behe, Michael J. *Darwin's Black Box*. New York, N.Y.: The Free Press, 1996.

Baker, Dr. Robin, chief contributing editor. *The Mystery of Migration*. New York, N.Y.: The Viking Press, 1981.

Comins, Neil F. *What If the Moon Didn't Exist?* New York, N.Y.: Harper Perennial, 1995.

Davies, Paul. *The Cosmic Blueprint*. Philadelphia, Pa.: Templeton Foundation Press, 2004.

Dembski, William A. *The Design Revolution*. Downers Grove, Ill.: InterVarsity Press, 2004.

Dembski, William A. *Intelligent Design*. Downers Grove, Ill.: InterVarsity Press, 1999.

Garland, Trudu Hammel. *Fascinating Fibonaccis*. Palo Alto, Calif.: Dale Seymour Publications, 1987.

Gonzalez, Guillermo, and J. W. Richards. *The Privileged Planet*. Washington, D.C.: Regnery Publishing Co., 2004.

Hoyle, Frederick. *The Intelligent Universe*. Holt, Rinehart & Winston, 1983.

Lester, Lane P., and Raymond G. Bohlin. *The Natural Limits to Biological Change*. Dallas, Tex.: Probe Ministries International, 1984.

Lovett, Sarah. *Encyclopedia of Extremely Weird Animals*. Santa Fe, N.M.: John Muir Publications, 1997.

Meyer, Stephen A. *Signature in the Cell*. HarperOne, 2009.

Page, Jake, and Eugene S. Morton. *Lords of the Air: The Smithsonian Book of Birds*. New York, N.Y.: Orion Books, Crown Publishers, 1989.

Ross, Hugh, and Fazale Rana. *Origins of Life*. Downers Grove, Ill.: InterVarsity Press, 2004.

Simmons, Geoffrey. *What Darwin Didn't Know*. Eugene, Oreg.: Harvest House Publishers, 2004

Thaxton, Charles B., Walter L. Bradley, and Roger L. Olsen. *The Mystery of Life's Origin*. New York, N.Y.: Philosophical Library, Inc., 1984.

Shklovskii, I.S., and Carl Sagan. *Intelligent Life in the Universe*. New York, N.Y.: Dell Publishing, 1966.

Wells, Jonathan. *The Politically Incorrect Guide to Darwinism and Intelligent Design*. Washington, D.C.: Regnery Pub., 2007.

Evolution

Teaching Science in a Climate of Controversy. Ipswich, Mass.: American Scientific Affiliation, 1986.

Behe, Michael J. *The Edge of Evolution*. New York, N.Y.: Free Press, 2007.

Collins, Francis. *The Language of God.* New York, N.Y.: Simon and Shuster, 2006.

Davis, Percival, and Dean Kenyon. *Of Pandas and People.* Dallas, Tex.: Haughton Publishing Co., 1989.

Dawkins, Richard. *The Blind Watchmaker.* New York, N.Y.: W. Norton & Co., Inc., 1986.

Denton, Michael. *Evolution: A Theory in Crisis.* Bethesda, Md.: Adler and Adler Publishers, Inc., 1985.

Denton, Michael. *Nature's Destiny.* New York, N.Y.: Simon & Schuster, Inc., 1998.

Eichman, Phillip. *Understanding Evolution.* Available from **Does God Exist?** 1555 Echo Valley Dr., Niles, MI 49120.

Gish, Duane T. *Evolution: The Fossils Still Say No.* El Cajon, Calif.: Institute for Creation Research, 1995.

Johanson, Donald, and Maitland Edey. *Lucy.* New York, N.Y.: Simon & Schuster, 1981.

Johnson, Phillip E. *Darwin on Trial.* Downers Grove, Ill.: InterVarsity Press, 1991.

Johnson, Phillip E. *Defeating Darwinism by Opening Minds.* Downers Grove, Ill.: InterVarsity Press, 1990.

Johnson, Phillip E. *Evolution as Dogma.* Dallas, Tex.: Haughton Publishing Co., 1990.

Johnson, Phillip E. *The Wedge of Truth.* Downers Grove, Ill.: InterVarsity Press, 2000.

Molnar, Stephen. *Human Variation.* Upper Saddle River, N.J.: Prentice Hall, 1998.

Newman, Robert C. and John L. Wiester. *What's Darwin Got to Do With It?* Downers Grove, Ill.: InterVarsity Press, 2000.

Numbers, Ronald L. *The Creationists.* New York, N.Y.: Alfred A. Knopf, 1992.

Ross, Hugh. *The Genesis Question.* Colorado Springs, Colo.: NavPress, 1994.

Ross, Hugh. *A Matter of Days.* Colorado Springs, Color.: NavPress, 2004.

Ross, Hugh, and Fazale Rana. *Who Was Adam?* Colorado Springs, Color.: NavPress, 2005.

Schaefer, Henry F. *Science and Christianity: Conflict or Coherence?* Watkinsville, Ga.: The Apollos Trust Publisher, 2004.

Spetner, Lee. *Not By Chance.* Brooklyn, N.Y.: The Judaica Press, 1997.

Wells, Jonathan. *Icons of Evolution.* Washington, D.C.: Regnery Publishing Inc., 2000.

Werner, Carl. *Evolution: The Grand Exiperiment*. Green Forest, Ark.: New Leaf Press, 2007.

Witham, Larry. *Where Darwin Meets the Bible: Creationists and Evolutionists in America*. New York, N.Y.: Oxford University Press, 2002.

The Paranormal and UFOs

Corliss, William R. *Science Frontiers: Some Anomalies and Curiosities of Nature*. Glen Arm, Md.: The Sourcebook Project, 1994.

Candland, Douglas Keith. *Feral Children and Clever Animals*. New York, N.Y.: Oxford University Press, 1993.

Cults, Spiritual Counterfeits Project, PO Box 4308, Berkeley, CA 94704.

Cults, Christian Research Journal, PO Box 7000, Rancho Santa Margarita, CA 92688-7000.

Geisler, Norman, and Ron Rhodes. *Correcting the Cults*. Grand Rapids, Mich.: Baker Books, 1997.

Jehovah Witness Material, Comments from the Friends, PO Box 840, Stoughton, MA 02072.

Klass, Philip J. *UFOs Explained*. New York, N.Y.: Random House, 1974.

Klass, Philip J. *UFOs: The Public Deceived*. Buffalo, N.Y.: Prometheus Books, 1983.

Randi, James. *The Mask of Nostradamus*. Buffalo, N.Y.: Prometheus Press, 1988.

Saler, Benson, Cha Green Forest, AR rles A. Zigler, and Charles B. Moore. *UFO Crash at Roswell: The Genesis of a Modern Myth*. Smithsonian Institution Press, 1997.

Story, Ronald. *Guardians of the Universe*. New York, N.Y.: St. Martins Press, 1980

Story, Ronald. *The Space-Gods Revealed*. New York, N.Y.: Harper & Row, 1974.

Tanner, Sandra, and Gerald. *Major Problems of Mormonism*. Salt Lake City, Utah: Utah Lighthouse Ministry, 1989.

Wohlberg, Steve. *End Time Delusions*. Shippensburg, Pa.: Destiny Image Publishers, Inc., 2004.

Philosophy and Morality

Caputo, Michael. *God Seen Through the Eyes of the Greatest Minds*. West Monroe, La.: Howard Publishing Co., 2000.

Chamberlain, Paul. *Can We Be Good Without God?* Downers Grove, Ill.: InterVarsity Press, 1996.

Chamberlain, Paul. *Good, Bad, and Ugly*. Downers Grove, Ill.: InterVarsity Press, 1996.

Chamberlain, Paul. *Whose Life Is It Anyway?* Norcross, Ga.: Ravi Zacharias International Ministries, 2002.

Cohen, Richard. *Coming Out Straight*. Winchester, Va.: Oakhill Press, 2000.

Cohen, Richard. *Gay Children—Straight Parents*. Downers Grove, Ill.: InterVarsity Press, 2007.

Craig, William Lane. *God, Are You There?* Norcross, Ga.: Ravi Zacharias International Ministries,. 1999.

Craig, William Lane. *What Does God Know?* Norcross, Ga.: Ravi Zacharias International Ministries, 2002.

Dallas, Joe. *A Strong Delusion*. Eugene, Oreg.: Harvest House Publishers, 1996.

Davies, Bob, and Anita Wortham. *Someone I Love is Gay*. Downers Grove, Ill.: InterVarsity Press, 1996.

Davies, Bob, and Lori Rentzel. *Coming Out of Homosexuality*. Downers Grove, Ill.: InterVarsity Press, 1993.

Davies, Paul. *The Mind of God*. New York, N.Y.: Simon & Schuster, 1992.

Einstein, Albert. *Ideas & Opinions*. New York, N.Y.: Bonanza Books, Crown Publishing Co., 1954.

Grant, George. *Grand Illusions: The Legacy of Planned Parenthood*. Brentwood, Tenn.: Wolgemuth & Hyatt Publishers, Inc., 1988.

Homosexual Issues, Exodus International, PO Box 540119, Orlando, FL 32854.

Jones, Stanton L., and Mark A. Yarhouse. *Homosexuality: The Use of Scientific Research in the Church's Moral Debate*. Downers Grove, Ill.: InterVarsity Press, 2000.

Kastleman, Mark. *The Drug of the New Millennium*. Granite Publishing, 2001.

Kushner, Harold. *Who Needs God*. New York, N.Y.: Summit Books, 1989.

Lewis, C. S. *Mere Christianity*. New York, N.Y.: The Macmillan Co., 1952.

McGrath, Alister E. *Intellectuals Don't Need God and Other Modern Myths*. Grand Rapids, Mich.: Zondervan Publishing House, 1993.

Moreland, J. P. *What Is The Soul?* Norcross, Ga.: Ravi Zacharias International Ministries, 2002.

Nicolosi, James, and Linda Ames Nicolosi. *A Parent's Guide to Preventing Homosexuality*. Downers Grove, Ill.: InterVarsity Press, 2002.

Owens, Virginia Stem. *And the Trees Clapped Their Hands.* Grand Rapids, Mich.: Wm. B. Eerdmans Publishing Co., 1984.

Penrose, Roger. *The Emperor's New Mind.* New York, N.Y.: Oxford University Press, 1990.

Schaeffer, Francis A. *A Christian Manifesto.* Wheaton, Ill.: Crossway Books, 1981.

Stetson, Brad, and Joseph Conti. *The Truth About Tolerance.* Downers Grove, Ill.: InterVarsity Press, 2005.

Taliaferro, Charles. *Does The Idea of God Make Sense?* Norcross, Ga.: Ravi Zacharias International Ministries, 2002.

Whitehead, Neil, and Brier. *My Genes Made Me Do It.* Lafayette, La.: Huntington House Publishers, 1999.

REFERENCES

CHAPTER 1

The Cosmos and the Creation

Andromeda. 1998. In *Britannica CD 99 Multimedia Edition* [CD. ROM]. Encyclopaedia Britannica, Inc.

Audouze, J., and G. Israel, eds. 1988. *The Cambridge Atlas of Astronomy*. Cambridge: Cambridge University Press.

Barrow, J. D. 1994. *The Origin of the Universe*. New York: Basic-Books (a division of HarperCollins Publishers, Inc.).

Dooling, D. 1998. Space Exploration: Unmanned Satellites. In *Britannica Book of the Year* [CD-ROM]. Encyclopaedia Britannica, Inc.

Hawking, S. W. 1988. *A Brief History of Time*. New York: Bantam Books.

http://www.americanhumanist.org/who_we_are/about_humanism/Humanist_Manifesto_I

Sagan, C. 1980. *Cosmos*. New York: Random House.

CHAPTER 2
The Design of Planet Earth

Smith. 1976. *The Human Degree*. J. B. Lippincott Co.

Flew, Antony. 2007. *There is a God: How the World's Most Notorious Atheist Changed His Mind*, Harper Collins Publishers.

CHAPTER 4
Design as Evidenced in Life

Coppedge, James. 1976. *Evolution: Possible or Impossible?* Grand Rapids, Mich. Zondervan Publishing.

Currie, C. R., J. A. Scott, R. C. Summerbell, and D. Malloch. 1999. Fungus-Growing Ants Use Antibiotic-Producing Bacteria to Control Garden Parasites. *Nature* 398.

Dawkins, R. 1986. *The Blind Watchmaker*. New York: W. W. Norton & Company.

de Duve, C. 1995. The Beginnings of Life on Earth. *American Scientist*, [On-line], September-October. Available: http://www. sigmaxi. org/amsci/ articles/95 articles/CdeDuve.html

Griffiths, A. J. E, J. H. , D. T. Suzuki, R. C. Lewontin, and W. M. Gelbart. 1993. *Genetic Analysis*. W. H. Freeman and Company.

Heyning, J. E., and J. G. Mead. 1997. Thermoregulation in the Mouths of Feeding Grey Whales. *Science* 278, 7 November.

Radetsky, P. 1998. Life's Crucible. *Earth*, February.

Schmidt-Nielsen, K. 1997. *Animal Physiology*. Cambridge University Press.

Schultz, T. R. 1999. Ants, Plants, and Antibiotics. *Nature* 398.

CHAPTER 5
The Nature of God

Abbot, E. 1994, reprint. *Flatland/Sphereland*. New York: Harper-Collins.

Williams, J. G. 1968. *Christian Faith and the Space Age*. New York: The World Publishing Co.

CHAPTER 6

Why Choose the Bible as the Word of God?

Branley and Wimmer. 1970. Concepts of the Universe. *Natural History* magazine, December.

DeHoff, G. 1959. *Why We Believe the Bible.* DeHoff Publications.

Grant, George. 1988. *Grand Illusions: The Legacy of Planned Parenthood.* Brentwood, Tenn.: Wolgemuth & Hyatt Publishers, Inc.

Prophecies Concerning the Messiah. 2000. [On-line], 17 March. Available: http://www.ccobb.org/prophecies_introduction.asp-Siegel, L. 1997. Scientists Unsure if Dinos Linked to Birds. *The Salt Lake Tribune* [On-line], 24 October. Available: http://www.sltrib.com/ old/97/ oct/l 02497 /nation_ w/3772.htm

Schmidt, Alvin. 2001. *Under the Influence.* Grand Rapids, Mich.: Zondervan Publishing.

CHAPTER 7

Why — Is There Evil?
— Do We Exist?
— Do We Suffer?

Sayers, D. L. 1969. *Christian Letters to a Post-Christian World.* Grand Rapids, Mich.: William B. Eerdmans Publishing Company.

CHAPTER 8

What about All Those Mistakes in The Bible?

Dawkins, Richard. 2006. *The God Delusion.* New York: Houghton Mifflin Company.

Dawkins, Richard. 1995. *River Out of Eden: A Darwin View of Life.* New York: Basic Books (a division of HarperCollins Publishers, Inc.).

McGarth, Alister, and Joanna Collicutt McGrath. 2007. *The Dawkins Delusion*. Downers Grove, Ill.: InterVarsity Press.

CHAPTER 9
Evolution

Collins, Francis, *The Language of God*, Simon & Shuster, Inc., 2006, ISBN-13:978-0-7432-8639-8, $26.00, hardback, 294 pages

Hartwig-Scherer, S. 1998. Apes or Ancestors? In W. A Dembski, ed. *Mere Creation Science, Faith & Intelligent Design*. Downers Grove, Ill.: InterVarsity Press.

Leiden, J. N. 1960. *Commentary of Nahmanides on Genesis 1-6*. New York: Brill Publishing.

Poirier, F. E., and J. D. McKee. 1999. *Understanding Human Evolution*. Upper Saddle River, N.J.: Prentice-Hall, Inc.

Sarna, N. N. 1989. *Genesis, the IPS Torah Commentary*. New York: Jewish Publication Society.

Willmington, H. L. 1982. *Willmington's Guide to the Bible*. Wheaton, IL: Tyndale House Publishers, Inc.

Wiseman, P. J. 1985. *Ancient Records and the Structure of Genesis*. Nashville: Thomas Nelson Publishers.

CHAPTER 10
The Age of the Earth

Brown, G. (Director and Editor), H. Morris, D. Gish, S. Austin, and A. Snelling (Moderators). 1996. *The Grand Canyon Catastrophe* [Videocassette]. (Available from Keziah and American Portrait Films, P. O. Box 19266, Cleveland, OH 44119).

Nelson, P., and J. Reynolds. 1999. Young Earth Creationism: Conclusion. In J. Moreland and J. Reynolds, eds. *Three Views on Creation and Evolution*. Grand Rapids, Mich.: Zondervan Publishing House.

Numbers, Ronald L. 2006. *The Creationists: From Scientific Creationism to Intelligent Design*. Cambridge, Mass.: Harvard University Press.

(*Questions Answered by Lipscomb and Sewell*, Gospel Advocate Co., Nashville, TN, 1974, page 747. Originally published by McQuiddy Printing Co. in 1921)

(*God's Prophetic Word* by Foy E. Wallace, The Roy E Cogdill Publishing Co., Lufkin, TX, 1946, page 6)

Robinson, B. 1996. Proving Evolution or Creation Science [Online]. Available: http://www.religioustolerance.org/ev_proof. htm.

Whitcomb, J., and H. Morris. 1961; 42nd reprint 1998. *The Genesis Flood*. Phillipsburg, N.J.: P & R Publishing.

CHAPTER 11

What Is Man?

Caldwell, M. 2000. Polly Wanna Ph.D.? *Discover* 21 0): January.

Clark, J. D. 1993. African and Asian Perspectives on Modem Human Origins. In M. J. Aitken, C. B. Stringer, and P. A. Mellars, eds. *The Origin of Modem Humans and the Impact of Chronometric Dating*. Princeton, N.J.: Princeton University Press.

Goldschmidt, R. B. 1940. *The Material Basis of Evolution*. New Haven, Conn.: Yale University Press.

Hauser, M. D. 2000. Morals, Apes, and Us. *Discover* 21 (2): February.

Hublin, J. J. 2000. An Evolutionary Odyssey [Review of the book *The Human Career: Human Biological and Cultural Origins* (second edition)]. *Nature* 403, 27 January.

Jones, S., R. Martin, and D. Pilbeam, eds. 1992. *The Cambridge Encyclopedia of Human Evolution*. Cambridge: Cambridge University Press.

Kellogg, Dr. Winthrop, articles about the study with Donald and Gua

Animals: Babe & Chimpanzee. *Time*, May.23.1932, http://www.time.com/time/magazine/article/0,9171,743764,00. html, retrieved, 3/15/2011

Chimpanzee excels baby in several mental tests. *ScienceNews*, Sept 17, 1932. Retrieved from http://www.sciencenews.org/view/generic/id/3124 on 3/15/2011.

Donald and Gua Kellogg at work-1931. http://pubpages.unh. edu/~jel/video/Kelloggs_V.html, retrieved 3/15/2011

Gua (chimpanzee). http://en.wikipedia.org/wiki/Gua_(chimpanzee), retrieved 3/15/2011.

Kellogg's Study: The Ape and the Child. http://www.audioblox2000.com/kellogg.html. retrieved 3/15/2011.

Klein, R. G. 1999. *The Human Career: Human Biological and Cultural Origins*. Chicago: The University of Chicago Press.

Lewin, R.1987. *Bones of Contention*. Chicago: The University of Chicago Press.

Renfrew, C. 1998. The Origins of World Linguistic Diversity: An Archaeological Perspective. In N. G. Jablonski and L. C. Aiello, eds. *The Origin and Diversification of Language*. San Francisco: California Academy of Sciences.

Tattersall, 1. 1995. *The Fossil Trail*. New York: Oxford University Press.

Tattersall, 1. 1998. *Becoming Human*. San Diego: Harcourt Brace & Company.

Thorndike. 1978. *Science News* 117, 19 August.

CHAPTER 12
Conclusion

Sheler, J. L., and J. M. Schrof. 1991. Religions's Search for a Common Ground with Science. Creation. U.S. News & World Report [On-line]. Available: http://www.usnews.com/usnews/news/create.htm

APPENDIX 3
String Theory

Green, B. 1999. *The Elegant Universe*. New York: W. W. Norton and Company, Inc.

Hawking, S. W. 1988. *A Brief History of Time*. New York: Bantam Books.

INDEX

A

Absolute 3, 17, 32, 57, 68
Adapt 46, 47, 105
Age of the earth 119
AIDS 75
American Sign Language 153
Amino acids 41–43
Amphibian(s) 133
Andromeda 6
Angels 87–90, 100
Angiosperm 209, 210
Angler fish 50
Animal 46, 47, 49, 50, 63, 75, 76, 104
Animal adaptations 49
Anthropomorphized 53
Antimatter 60, 86
Ant(s) 47, 48, 51, 63
Ape(s) 143, 148, 150
Arctic 49
Asah 109, 110, 111, 126, 202, 203, 205–207
Asteroid 22, 124, 132
Astronomy 4, 11, 24, 76, 77

Atheist(s) 1, 2, 6, 12, 13, 17, 27, 53, 60, 61, 85, 93, 95, 96, 98, 101, 105
Atlantic Ocean 128
Atlas 77
Atmospheric gases 24, 35, 41
Atom(s) 12, 26, 29–31, 34, 35–37, 57, 186
Australia 123

B

Backward rotation 22
Bacteria 39, 74, 76
Baptism 68, 131
Bara 109, 110, 111, 127, 201, 204–207
Bees 51
Beginning 1, 2, 3, 6, 8, 10, 12,–15, 17, 18, 51, 52, 56, 58, 59, 61, 63, 66, 78, 80, 107
Behemah 128, 131, 204, 205, 207, 211
Bhagavad-Gita 65

Bible 1, 2, 18, 45, 52, 57–59, 61, 62,
   64–67, 70, 71, 77–83, 85, 87,
   88, 90, 95, 96, 99, 100, 101,
   103, 105–112
Biblical kinds 105
Bifocal eyes 50
Big bang 9, 10, 13, 18, 19, 29,
   31–33, 54, 158, 189, 191, 192
Bird(s) 49, 51, 63, 105, 106, 130, 134
Black hole 13, 25
Bloodletting 72
Bone(s) 115, 123, 138, 141
Brain size 143
Burgess Shale 158

C

Cambrian explosion 158
Cambrian period 121, 130, 133
Capacity for language 155
Carbon 30, 186
Carbon dioxide 43
Cattle 103, 128, 131, 204, 207, 211
Caveman 148, 149
Chemical codes 26
Chengjiang fossils 158
Chimpanzee(s) 104, 145, 146, 151,
   152
Chromosome 41
Closed system 12
Cloud cover 22
Coal 123
COBE (Cosmic Background Explorer)
   9
Coincidence 50, 74, 79, 112
Cold-blooded 134
Comet 25, 45
Conditioning 154
Conifers 125, 129, 132
Consciousness 148, 155
Convection 37
Core 123
Cosmology 6, 13
Cosmos 4, 8–13, 17, 37, 45, 49
Created life 105

Creation myths 106
Culture(s) 76, 96, 98, 107, 109, 145

D

Dark Ages 75, 143
Dark pigmentation 46
Darwin 40
Dating methods 116, 141
Dawkins, Richard 50, 95, 96
Definition of life 39
Deshe 128, 207
Design 15, 18, 22, 23, 29, 35, 37, 39,
   45–48, 50
Designer/creator 34
Dimensions 6, 14, 32, 56, 58, 59, 78
Dinosaur 115, 123–125, 130, 131
Disease-carrying organisms 75
DNA 26, 27, 39, 40, 41, 43, 46, 49,
   105, 107, 111
Dogs 103, 104
Dolphin 49
Dualism 87
Dust 19, 45, 110, 117, 121, 137, 151

E

Earthquakes 76, 120, 124
Earth's history 42, 158, 159
Earth's magnetic field 24
Earth's tilted axis 24
Ecological system 48
Ecosystematic Design 48
Einstein, Albert 9, 60, 61, 185, 189
Electromagnetic force 30, 31, 33
Electron(s) 9, 13, 29, 30, 32, 34, 57,
   60, 86
Element(s) 26, 27, 30, 34, 64, 78,
   107, 120, 124, 137, 153
Elephant(s) 76, 77
Embryonic development 123
Environment(s) 36, 39, 46, 47, 49, 51,
   53, 72, 81, 105
Erets 126
Eseb 128, 207

Europe(an) 75, 115, 123, 128
Eve 47, 73, 118, 144
Evil 67, 81, 85 – 93
Evolution 33, 46, 47, 103 – 105, 111
Expanding universe 7, 29, 33, 126

F

Fallen angel 87, 88
Family 1, 80, 92, 97, 106, 119, 150
Feathered serpents 106
Fern 125, 129, 132
Flatland 54 – 57, 59
Flesh and blood 57, 90, 138, 151
Flippers 49
Flood 99, 120 – 122, 124, 186
Flood geology 120, 121
Fossil record 120, 124, 125, 129, 135,
   143, 148 – 150, 159
Fossil(s) 111, 115, 120, 123, 125, 126,
   129, 133, 138, 140, 141, 144,
   146, 148, 158, 159
Four fundamental forces 29, 30, 32,
   33, 58, 189
Free will 88, 89, 91, 92
Fulfilled prophecy 68

G

Galaxies 4, 6, 7, 8, 9, 13, 19, 29, 31,
   32, 86
Garden of Eden 118
Genesis 107, 114, 118, 120, 126 – 132,
   134, 137, 150, 158, 159, 201
Genetics 115
Genome 105
Geologic column 121
Glen Rose 125
Global temperature 24

God 1, 2, 9, 14, 17, 27, 32 – 34, 37,
   39, 45, 52, 53, 56 – 68, 70, – 72,
   75 – 78, 80 – 83, 85 – 93, 95,
   97 – 100, 103, 105 – 112,
   114, 115, 117, 118, 120, 121,
   124 – 127, 129, 132, 137,
   143, 147, 150, 151, 153, 155,
   157 – 159, 190
God'S purpose in creating 89
God's skin color 62
Goodall, Jane 148
Good and evil 85, 90, 92
Grand Canyon 115, 121, 122, 127
Grand Unified Theory 58
Gravity 10, 13, 31 – 33, 185, 186
Gua 152
Gymnosperm 125, 129, 132, 207

H

Hand washing 74
Hate 80, 88
Hawking, Stephen 10, 189
Heat death 13
Heaven 56, 62, 63, 66, 67, 76, 78, 87,
   91, 106, 108
Hebrew 71, 72, 99, 105, 108, 109, 111
Heredity 142
Hexagon 51
Hindu 66, 76
Holy books 65, 66
Homer 66
Hominid 106, 138, 144, 146, – 150
Horse 104
Horsetail 129
Hubble telescope 6, 21
Human characteristics 53, 59, 148,
   153 – 155
Human Genome 105
Humanist Manifesto 6
Human spirit 110
Hybridization 103
Hydrogen 10, 11, 32, 34, 35

I

Image 53, 58, 59, 68, 85–87, 90, 108, 110, 132, 137, 147, 150, 151, 153, 155, 159, 210
Image of God 137, 150, 151, 153, 155, 159
Immanuel 82
Inorganic chemicals 49
Insect(s) 47, 48, 50, 117, 133, 154
Instinct 50, 51, 144, 145, 154
Intelligence Quotient 151
Intelligent design 29, 39, 48, 50, 157, 159
Intelligent quotient (IQ) 66, 151, 154
Iridium 124
Irreducibly complex 40, 48

J

Jupiter 24

K

K dwarfs 21
Kellogg, Dr. Winthrop 152
Kind (biblical use in Genesis 1) 105, 106, 111
King James 99, 109, 201
Knuckle walkers 150
Koran 65, 67, 68, 70

L

Language 41, 71, 98, 100, 108, 109
Law of parity 85, 86
Leakey, Louis 141, 148
Lemur 148
Light-years 5, 6, 183, 191
Limestone 122
Love 57, 58, 81, 85–89, 92, 106, 152
Lumper(s) 141, 143

M

Magellanic clouds 6

Mammal(s) 51, 130, 133, 148, 150, 209
Marsupial 51
Mass(es) 4, 10, 13, 17, 31, 57, 59
Master Designer 46
Mathematical probabilities 18
Matter 3, 4, 10, 17, 18, 25, 26, 29–33, 54, 57, 58, 78, 86, 87, 110
Melanin 46
Metabolism 46
Metamorphic 121
Metaphors for God 59
Metaphysical 155
Methuselah 96
Microevolution 104, 143
Mid-Atlantic Ridge 128
Milky Way 5, 6, 19, 20, 192
Miller, Stanley 41–43, 49
Miraculous 51, 57, 68, 76, 87, 109, 110, 126
Missing link 138, 143
Monkey(s) 103, 104, 138, 140, 144
Morality 80
Mormon 65
Moses 72, 74–77, 97, 98, 106, 108
Mother Eve 47
Muhammad 68
Multiple stars 21
Mutation 46, 158

N

Natural selection 158
Nebraskan man 140
Neutrino(s) 13, 29, 57
New Testament 67, 82, 100, 105, 130, 134
Newton, Isaac 8, 77, 185
Nitrogen 30, 43
Noah 79, 99, 119, 122, 124
Northern Hemisphere 23, 24
Nucleotide(s) 41

O

Ocean current 24
Old Testament 67, 70, 100
Omnipresent 62
Organism 39, 40, 47, 50, 75
Original language 71
Origin of matter 3
Oscillating universe 13
Oxygen 30, 34, 35, 49

P

Parity 85–88
Particle accelerator 60
Pavlov, Ivan 154
Pentateuch 106
Pepperberg, Irene 155
Photosynthesis 49
Phyla 134
Physical science(s) 17, 60, 77, 158
Planck time 10, 33
Pollution problems 75
Polyandry (multiple husbands) 80
Polygamy (multiple wives) 80, 100
Polymer(s) 43
Porpoise(s) 151
Prebiotic (lifeless) 43
Prehistoric 130, 140, 149
Primates 159
Primitive cultures 107
Primitive earth 42, 44, 129
Primordial soup 40
Principle of Equivalence 61
Probabilities 18, 19, 26, 43, 183
Proboscis monkey 138, 140
Process of succession 129
Properties of God 57, 58
Prophecy 68
Proteins 40–43, 192
Protein synthesis 40
Protoavis 130
Protoplasm 40
Punctuated equilibrium 112, 130, 159

Q

Quarantine 74, 75

R

Race(s) 47, 63, 104, 141
Radioactive decay 30
Random chance 44, 51
Red dwarf(s) 21
Red giant(s) 21, 22
Relative dating 141
RNA (ribonucleic acid) 39, 41, 43
Roche's Limit 21, 22
Rocks 116, 120–125, 128, 129, 134, 146
Roman soldier 81
Romulus and Remus 72

S

Sagan, Carl 12, 67
Sapiens 106
Satan 87–92
Saturn 24
Scopes monkey trial 140
Second law of thermodynamics 12
Sedimentary 116, 121
Self 155
Seven-day week 106
Seyfert galaxy 19
Shamayim 126, 209
Simple to complex 120
Singularity 8, 9, 13, 32, 54
Skeleton(s) 138, 139, 149, 150
Skin color 46, 47, 62, 142
Skull 143, 149
Soil 35, 48, 120
Solar system 5, 19, 21, 22, 24, 25, 86
Sons of God 88
Soul 144, 148, 149, 151, 155
Southern Hemisphere 23, 24
Species 46, 47, 104, 105, 106, 129, 131, 141, 143, 208
Speech 46, 155
Spencer, Hubert 78

Spiritual 64, 65, 87, 90, 98, 110, 144, 151, 152, 155
Splitters 141, 143
Star(s) 4, 6, 9, 11, 19, 21, 22, 24, 31, 33, 45, 126, 191, 192, 208
Stoner, Peter 68, 69
Stone tools 144 – 147, 150
Strong force 30, 31
Subatomic 30, 57, 60
Succession 129
Suffering 82, 85, 91 – 93
Sun 4, 5, 10 – 12, 21, 22 – 25, 31, 46, 77, 100, 106, 108, 126
Supernatural 70, 76, 154
Supreme Being 154
Symbiosis 47, 48
Symbiotic relationship 47

T

Taxonomy 106
Thermodynamics 12
Thorndike, Edward 153
Time-Life 148
Time line 32, 33
Time(s) 2, 7, 8, 10, 14, 32, 40, 44, 45, 47, 48, 50, 51, 53, 56, 58, 59, 60 – 63, 66, 72, 75 – 79, 81, 87, 91, 95, 97, 100, 108, 111, 113, 116 – 118, 122, 124, 125, 129, 141, 143, 146, 150, 153, 158, 159, 189, 190, 191, 193
Tongues 49
Tool kit 111
Tools 39, 90, 144, 146, 150
Tooth 115, 140, 149
Transfiguration 68
Translation 2, 41, 71, 99, 108, 109
Trial-and-error 51, 78
Trial-and-error learning 51
Turtles 51

U

Ungulate 128, 131

Unified force 33
Unified Force 32
Uniformitarianism 115, 124, 159
Unintelligent chance 34
Universal laws 17
Upanishads 65
Ussher, Bishop James 117

V

Variability of time 60
Vedas 65, 66, 68
Venus 22
Volcanic eruptions 120
Vultures 76

W

Washoe 153
Water molecule 34 – 37, 186
Water(s) 22 – 24, 32, 34 – 37, 42, 46, 49, 50, 79, 116, 118, 120, 122, 123, 127, 129, 130, 158, 186
Weak Force 30
Whales 49
White 46, 59, 67
White, 148
White dwarf 21
White hair 59
Woman's seed 73
Women 46, 72 – 74, 80, 89
Worms 76, 133
Worship 77, 106, 115, 151, 154
Writing 66 – 68, 70, 74, 76 – 79, 97, 98

Y

Yatsar 109, 110
Young earth 120, 121